Pompeii

Images from the buried cities

Ministero per i Beni e le Attività Culturali

SOPRINTENDENZA
ARCHEOLOGICA
DI POMPEI

Pompeii

Images from the buried cities

Electa Napoli

Electa Napoli

Editing
Silvia Cassani
Paola Rivazio

Graphics
Enrica D'Aguanno
Gianni Manna

Translations
Stella Cragie
Colum Fordham (nos. 45-47a-b.)

Pompeii
Images from the buried cities

ABERDEEN
CITY COUNCIL

Aberdeen Art Gallery
19th June - 4th August 2001

Exhibition curator
Pietro Giovanni Guzzo

Scientific research
Gina Carla Ascione
Giovanna Bonifacio
Caterina Cicirelli
Antonio d'Ambrosio
Ernesto De Carolis
Lorenzo Fergola
Maria Paola Guidobaldi
Marisa Mastroroberto
Mario Pagano
Anna Maria Sodo
Grete Stefani
Antonio Varone

Co-ordination
Gina Carla Ascione
Santino D'Antonio
Anna Matrone

Exhibition installation
Valerio Papaccio
Maria Emma Pirozzi
Direction of restoration work
Gina Carla Ascione
Giovanna Bonifacio
Ernesto De Carolis
Lorenzo Fergola
Mario Pagano
Anna Maria Sodo

Restoration
Soprintendenza Archeologica
di Pompei
Michele Allocca
Ciro Buondonno
Pasquale Esposito
Giuseppe Farella
Luigi Giordano
Stefania Giudice
Michele Iuzzino
Michele Pellì
Antonio Rinaldi
Vincenzo Serrapica
Ernesto Siano
Gioacchino Sicignano
Manuela Valentini
Stefano Vanacore
Giuseppe Zuccherino
Ambra Restauri
Artex Restauro
Cinzia Autieri s.n.c.
Ditta Ciro Nastri
Francesco Esposito
Euro di Giancarlo Napoli

The restoration of the majority of the
frescoes was made possible by the
generous contribution of the Japanese
Museums of Yokohama and Fukuoka.
Contributions to the restoration were
also made by the Rotary Club of Torre
del Greco and the Banca di Credito
Popolare of Torre del Greco

Graphics
Michele Caiazzo
Ubaldo Pastore

Archaeology custodians
Giacomo Arnone
Anna Cozzolino
Tommasina Di Mauro
Andrea Esposito
Mosè Improta
Antonio Martucci
Giovanni Masullo
Vincenzo Matrone
Ciro Sicignano
Luigi Sirano
Ferdinando Staiano

Photography
Archives of the Soprintendenza
Archeologica di Pompei
Gianni Falconieri and Paola Teti
Luciano Pedicini-Archivio dell'Arte, Naples
© Copyright of the images: Ministero
per i Beni e le Attività Culturali
Soprintendenza Archeologica di Pompei

Authors of the entries
Giovanna Bonifacio   (G.B.)
Caterina Cicirelli   (C.C.)
Ernesto De Carolis   (E.D.C.)
Lorenzo Fergola   (L.F.)
Marisa Mastroroberto   (M.M.)
Mario Pagano   (M.P.)
Anna Maria Sodo   (A.M.S.)
Grete Stefani   (G.S.)
Antonio Varone   (A.V.)

Accademia Italiana, London

Director
Rosa Maria Letts

Assistant
Jenny Elliott

Exhibition Officers
Shaun Dolan
Georgina Dennis

Development Officer
Benedicta Marzinotto

Graphic design
Mannion Design

The exhibition is insured by
Progress Insurance Brokers

The Accademia Italiana and the
Aberdeen Art Gallery wish to thank Agip
(UK) Limited most sincerely for their
support for this exhibition, without
which it would not have taken place

Contents

Preface

"Paintings from the Buried Cities" *was an exhibition I first saw in 1999 on an early spring morning outside Naples in the Royal Palace of Portici which we had reached by train from Rome and by the Vesuviana, the local line that runs from Naples along the bay skirting the foothills of Vesuvius. The five-hour journey was worthwhile in order to spend two hours in isolation among the precious images which spoke, from the elegant palace walls, of a past and buried civilization. It brought their houses to life, their walls were with myths and fables to accompany and reflect their inhabitants' enchantment for the beauty they saw around them. They had created a unique marriage of sea views seen from their houses which faced the incredible Naples bay and the vistas their owners had recreated on their parietal walls to reflect it.*

Paintings by the warmest glowing colours – ochres, deep reds, oranges, greens and yellows – incredible to imagine without seeing them in their real sites, were the ones which lit the last golden days of a society of Campanian landlords, Roman politicians and business men. This wealthy and powerful community knew that they were risking fate remaining in the shadow of Vesuvius, as the area had already suffered an earthquake in 62 AD, which destroyed many parts of those beautiful towns. It was dangerous to continue to live in the Vesuvian area but the citizens decided to start a new brave process of restoration, which was enthusiastically agreed to by the emperor, so they remained. Perhaps they tried to defy the famous statement "Vedi Napoli e poi muori" which we all know and understand: "See Naples and die". Fate in the hands of Vesuvius did strike again and on 24th August 79 AD, the mountain erupted in the most spectacular way, bright and magnificent at first, turning into ashes and finally into dark and hardened lava by the time it enveloped the last of the towns, beautiful Herculaneum. Death and silence followed – eventually oblivion overtook the memory of their lives.

Now some of the treasures from these towns excavated in the 18th and 19th centuries, and finally by the Soprintendenza of Pompeii in the 20th Century, have miraculously been made available to us to present in Aberdeen in Scotland by the shores of the North Sea. The original exhibition of "Paintings from the Buried Cities" has been partly recreated with the addition of some amazing statuary from the Royal Villa of Oplontis. Some newly discovered frescoes, recently unearthed, have also been included and new catalogue articles and entries have been written.

The Accademia Italiana, an institution totally dedicated to the presentation of Italian art in Great Britain, is proud to present this exhibition which has been made possible only because of the generosity and kind co-operation of Professor Pietro Giovanni Guzzo, the Soprintendente of Pompeii, the dedicated knowledge and scholarship of Dr. Gina Carla Ascione and other experts, together with the intelligent design and installation by Architects Valerio Papaccio and Maria Emma Pirozzi, who have recreated for us an eruption of colour and art no longer buried but captured by their expert hand.

The Accademia Italiana also wishes to express its most grateful thanks to Agip (UK) Limited, part of Eni the Italian integrated energy group committed to supporting arts and culture worldwide. Agip (UK) Limited has worked in partnership with Aberdeen City Council to bring this unique free exhibition to Aberdeen Art Gallery.

Rosa Maria Letts
Accademia Italiana

Introduction

The exhibition in foreign countries of antiquities which are deeply rooted in the specific historical and geographical context of another country, though now standard practice, is fraught with risks. Having to resort to selection, summaries and reduction means running the risk of presenting a one-sided picture of a cultural reality, the complexity of which may not be fully understood or appropriately interpreted as a result.

If, as in the case of the ancient towns buried by the eruption of Mt Vesuvius in 79 AD, the over-riding impression one receives is of wonder rather than the catastrophic events which took place, then the risk appears considerable.

However, trying to avoid this pitfall altogether results in a failure to achieve an objective view of those far-off times. They are still seen through the fanciful interpretation of Bulwer-Lytton, rather than the painstaking work of archeologists and historians, the technicalities of whose work may well appear a world apart to non-specialists.

One of the aims of this exhibition is to show the British public the difference between these two approaches to an interpretation of this historical period in the Vesuvian area. In fact, Britain has made a considerable contribution to our knowledge about it, through her poets, novelists, archeologists and scholars of ancient history, who have studied and written about the fate of these Vesuvian towns, providing us with a fresh approach to the subject.

We sincerely hope that the visitors to this exhibition will find it enjoyable and inspiring. For our part, we shall continue to do our utmost to preserve the "aura" of these sites which have been famous the world over for the last two hundred years or so, and to build on the knowledge we have acquired so far by conducting appropriate and objective research.

Pietro Giovanni Guzzo
Archaeological Superintendent of Pompeii

Wall paintings in the ancient Vesuvian towns reveal a picture of society
Antonio Varone

The tremendous eruption of Vesuvius on 24th August 79 AD has provided us with information about the organisation of daily life in Roman times which would otherwise have been lost forever.

The lava and ash erupted by Vesuvius covered a large area including whole towns – rich villas by the sea, estates and farms whose agriculture benefited from the fertile land – effectively turning the whole area into a "time capsule". Buried with the towns was the infrastructure which supported the daily life of a relatively important region in the early Roman Empire and the complex structure of society of this period revealed in its entirety – a truly unique microcosm, which has defined our vision of Roman times.

The first excavations of the Vesuvian towns were systematically carried out in the first half of the 18th century by King Charles III of Bourbon – a monarch whose contribution has yet to be fully recognised. These excavations were to influence the very concept and role of archeology. In effect, in the Vesuvian area after a hesitant start a "modern" vision of archeology began to emerge, which would evolve from merely salvaging objects to put in collections to the retrieval of information about the organisation of the Roman world in cultural as well as material and pragmatic terms.

The study of the Vesuvian towns has benefited from the preservation of the dimensions of space and time, shedding light on life in Campania in the first century AD in the wider context of Roman Italy. The discoveries made in the Vesuvian towns have significantly contributed to our knowledge of the period; for instance, what we know today about electoral propaganda is based almost entirely on discoveries made at Pompeii.

However, the enormous amount of discoveries has produced a plethora of evidence, that goes beyond the findings of traditional archeological research conducted on other sites – a situation which has meant that researchers have concentrated on analysing the situation during the last decades of life in these areas. This subject is so complex that many questions remain unanswered and just the tip of the iceberg has been revealed. Only in the last few years have the various strata been systematically excavated, studying the different phases which over many centuries have determined the formation and development of the Vesuvian towns in the wider historical context of Roman Italy. In the future, diachronic analysis will be the major focus of research, to complement the substantial progress made in synchronic studies relating to the early Roman Empire. This will enable researchers to move beyond the mere historical details of a building or site and learn more about the events that marked the development of life in pre-Roman Italy, helping us to understand the effects of these events on life at the time.

In one area in particular – the study of wall decorations in the Vesuvian towns – it has been possible to follow conceptual and semantic development, rather than artistic development, at least since the third century BC. This has provided us with interesting and valuable information, which helps in understanding the society of the times and its gradual evolution.

August Mau, undoubtedly the most expert and intelligent scholar of Vesuvian sites, pointed out that in some cases the wall decoration had been left intact for several generations, enabling him to develop a scheme (still used today) of classifying styles, each one linked to a specific historical period.

Apparently, the preservation of these paintings down the centuries, or the imitation of the paintings in rooms of the same house, was a deliberate act, no doubt due to the awareness of the status symbol of such works (a typical feature in Roman society) in the social values of many Roman families.

The study of these different styles, which are described more fully in another essay, provide us with important information and correlations regarding the cultural configuration of Vesuvian society in various periods of history.

The oldest extant wall decoration places Vesuvian society in the wider context of Hellenistic culture. Campania in the Samnite period subscribed to the values of *koiné*, which developed from Greece, spreading out and penetrating as far as the fringes of the Greek world.

Though evidence from earlier periods consists almost

Pompeii, House of the Ceii in 1916

Pompeii, House of Loreius Tiburtinus
in 1920

18 entirely of funerary painting, in Italy the culture, and particularly art, of the Samnites and the Etruscans was strongly influenced by the Greeks. For both peoples contact with Greece, especially through Greek colonies in the south of Italy, helped to foster a process of assimilation which acted as a cultural substratum and blended in with their own diverse cultures.

The conflict between the Samnite and Roman civilisations and the defeat of the Samnites by the Romans have produced accounts which were one-sided and superficial, and only archeological discoveries have been able to redress the balance. The fact that Cicero mentioned the philosophical symposia held in Taranto by Archita, Plato and Gaius Pontius Sannita (father of the *condottiero* who defeated the Romans at the Caudine Forks) suggests that the Samnite aristocracy was already deeply rooted in the sophisticated cultural milieu of the Greek world by the middle of the fourth century.

So it is not really surprising to learn that the oldest examples of wall painting in the Vesuvian area were inspired by the formal and artistic language current throughout the Greek world from Macedonia and Thrace to Egypt and even Iberia. In fact, there are similarities and interesting comparisons to be made with works in a number of areas under Greek influence and in Greece itself.

What is more significant is that the assimilation of these models became more direct and evident after the opening of free ports serving the oriental markets which the Mediterranean power of Rome was able to give its Italic allies during the second century AD. Clearly, direct and continuous contact at ports like Delos gave a society already deeply imbued with Greek culture even greater exposure to Greek patterns and life-styles. The assimilation of these forms was influenced by their own political and social organisation and led to the construction of majestic palaces built in the towns, residences of the "princely citizens", where wall painting became an architectural feature in addition to a purely aesthetic one.

After Rome conquered the region, following a number of conflicts, culture was completely transformed. Rome was slow to embrace the Hellenistic culture, and suspicious of it, though Greek culture and art was revisited through deeply rooted Roman traditions and based on their own expectations. By the end of the second century BC, Rome was the most cosmopolitan of all the cities of the world that it now virtually dominated. The custom of representing architecture through the medium of painting – called *oikoumene* – continued to develop independently, and eventually evolved into a unique formal style, ranging from organic unity to abstraction: in effect, from illusion to allusion.

In the Vesuvian area new settlers replaced local people in positions of power, though the figurative and artistic language did not undergo any rapid transformation, as it was part of a shared aesthetic tradition, though the new artistic tendencies were inspired by Rome. Though the second style may appear to go little further than developing the first, in fact the language it expressed was typically Roman – the fruit of a semantic development and evolution of content which can only be understood in the context of the diverse and complex organisation of Roman society.

Significantly, the most important examples of the new culture came from the suburban villas, where the concept of Roman aristocratic "villa life" found its best expression, perceived as essential to balance the *negotium* of busy political life in the town, and the *otium* of reflection, conversation and banquets.

In the first style, painting shows an organic depiction of the architectural components of buildings with *trompe l'oeil* representations giving the *illusion* of space and depth. These models were developed into *illusionist realism* of architectural features in an effort to extend the actual space of the room by "opening up" the wall behind the painting, with flights of columns disappearing into the background and lines of buildings melting into the distance. In this pictorial illusion the room opens onto the outside world and becomes part of it, revealing distant landscapes as if through the windows of a villa, where life flows by peacefully and innocuously.

After the upheavals of the civil wars, Vesuvian society entered a new period of peace with the advent of the Empire. During the early Roman Empire there were new settlers among the old Samnite or colonial families –

foreigners and freedmen who had moved to the Bay of Naples. It was here that the Imperial court and the Roman aristocracy spent their leisure time, attracted by the opportunity to find fortune and engage in trade. The position of the port of Pompeii, in particular, was strategically important and the town became a crossroads on the trade routes between Campania and the East, especially Alexandria. Such was the popularity (virtually an obsession) of Alexandria that it became a continual source of inspiration for the decoration of interiors.

The image of this very diverse society in the early Roman Empire is revealed in paintings of the third style. The animated compositions of the second style were abandoned after the political upheavals died down, and the search for a new formal, austere equilibrium evoking the past marked both the life and the art of the period. The world was part of a well-defined stable system, and this sense of measured order seemed to be reflected in the pictorial compositions. In earlier works the wall had been entirely covered with painting, whereas now it became the vehicle for individual expressions of ornamental and imaginary painting. The decorative style for rooms in vogue at the time used painting to illustrate social features and hierarchies in the form of *social allusion*. Painting was no longer a descriptive representation of reality, rather merely an allusion to reality, and it developed its own symbolic language in which the architectural elements became ornamental sections and columns were stele of vegetation or candelabra. By then painting had ceased to imitate architecture and was able to develop its own figurative language. Within the accepted guidelines which divided and prioritised the spaces, the artist's imagination – like the spirit of the peaceful times in which the people lived – could freely and realistically reveal and express the tranquillity and pleasures of life.

The Claudian-Neronian period brought with it rapid changes in lifestyle and taste. Conscious of their own fortune and with the austerity and sobriety desired in the Augustan period now a distant memory, people of this period liberally indulged in exaggeration and excess in a totally hedonistic lifestyle, in a desperate attempt to amaze and stun, rendering exceptional events the norm. This period marked the beginning of a swift though marked social transformation, mainly due to the liberty granted to the freedmen by Imperial power in a deliberate attempt to oppose the senators. These freedmen were often foreigners, industrious entrepreneurs or merchants, who were not bound by the limitations of *gravitas* and *dignitas* in the pursuit of wealth like the old traditional families; in fact, they had accumulated vast fortunes and were now the driving force of society. The earthquake of 62 AD in the Vesuvian area provided the opportunity for wholescale reconstruction and enabled the nouveaux riches to embark on lucrative financial ventures and architectural redevelopment. As a result, prestigious buildings changed hands and were turned into commercial premises, which enabled the bourgeois and eventually their descendants to climb up the social ladder.

The loss of measure and equilibrium typical of this period is inevitably reflected in the wall paintings. The sober decorations of the third style were gradually replaced by the ornate and theatrical exuberance of the new style of painting, while in Rome the austere villa of Augustus was replaced by the excessive ostentation of Nero's *Domus Aurea*. In this style the wall – which opens out in complicated perspectives of *trompe l'oeil* architecture has nothing in common with the practicality of the second style and once more became an allusion to, and the manifestation of, the pursuit and achievement of wealth.

The fourth style generally reflects the frenetic lifestyle of a society in which the emerging classes are represented by the rough-and-ready character Petronian Trimalchio, who symbolises many personalities in the Vesuvian area in the years immediately preceding the catastrophe.

Pompeian wall painting
Antonio d'Ambrosio

The wall paintings on plaster are among the most vivid and interesting remains preserved in the Vesuvian towns. Intended to cover and decorate the walls, they were also intended to indicate the importance of the various rooms in the house, though possibly not their functions. An account of the first systematic study of wall paintings, published by August Mau in 1882, proposed a classification in four "styles" (or decorative schemes) which ran chronologically, in Pompeii as in Rome, from the 2nd century BC to the 1st century AD – a classification which is still generally accepted today.

The "1st style", recorded in Greece and the eastern Mediterranean as early as the 4th-3rd century BC, spread westwards in the 2nd century and was in use until the beginning of the 1st century BC. This is not a painting as such, as it goes no further than using sections of coloured plaster in relief to imitate a wall built in regular stone blocks or covered with slabs of polychrome marble. This type of decoration consists of a socle, usually in a dark colour, a series of large vertical slabs in the central part of the wall followed by rows of blocks in the upper part, finishing in a cornice in relief which separates the wall from the ceiling. One of the typical features of Pompeian decoration compared to Greek and eastern Mediterranean examples is that the walls are considered individual elements. The decorative theme continues from one wall to the next without any interruption, so the blocks of one wall seem to flow into the next. This predominantly architectural style also features pictorial elements, such as the cubes in perspective which sometimes appear on the socle or the festoons usually painted on the upper part of the wall.

This decorative scheme was used in both private and public architecture, inside as well as outside. Some of the best examples are to be found in Pompeii, at the House of Sallust, the House of the Faun and the Basilica.

The "2nd style", which emerged at the end of the 2nd century BC, only began to take shape in the early 1st century. At first it was little more than an imitation of the structure of the wall, which had been achieved using relief in the 1st style. However, there was soon a sea-change in style: from painting a wall which was closed off and flat there developed a representation of real architectural elements painted in perspective on several storeys. The socle of the wall developed into a podium which seem to invade the room, supporting columns with architraves and ceilings which appear to project beyond the wall. Using this technique the wall creates an illusion of space and depth and opens up vistas through windows showing scenes beyond the wall, such as sanctuaries and distant landscapes, apparently in an attempt to escape the reality of the room. There is still much debate about the causes and inspiration which gave rise to this innovative decoration: was it a natural development of the previous style, the influence of Hellenistic architecture or of stage sets?

What is certain is that the artists who gradually introduced the 2nd style were inspired by all these sources, revisiting them with innovations. Their work was only loosely realistic and aimed to transport the owner of the house to a luxurious and imaginary place, giving him the sensation of inhabiting a great palace of the Greek dynasties. The climax of this style was reached in the mid 1st century BC with the splendid paintings in the villas of Poppaea at Oplontis and of P. Fannius Synistor at Boscoreale. Subsequent development consisted of a gradual reduction of the plastic and realistic elements of the architecture, which tended to become more rigid and stylised, eventually being reduced to just the cornice of the central decoration, which usually dominated the scene. While the interest in the depiction of spatial depth began to decline and the *trompe l'oeil* vista on the wall became less important, the decoration of the architectural elements became pre-eminent, and increasingly unreal and imaginary. The decoration evolving towards the scheme later known as the 3rd style was to become established a few years later.

Another type of decoration was also prevalent in the 2nd style: the *megalografia*, a scene with almost life-size figures represented in movement in the architectural settings, the best known example of which is the famous frieze at the Villa of the Mysteries.

In the "3rd style", which began in the early Augustan period, there is a move away from views of architecture in perspective and *trompe l'oeil*. The wall is divided into three equal sections vertically (socle, central part, upper part) and horizontally, with large monochrome panels showing borders of slender architectural, vegetal or simply linear elements containing decorative motifs. The central panel is the most important, usually containing a niche with a large picture of a mythological subject. Consequently, the surfaces of the walls once more became a closed plane, without any scenes in perspective or *trompe l'oeil* vistas, which defined the form of the room. Vestiges of the architectural elements remain in the central niche, particularly in the upper part of the wall, though they are reduced to simplistic motifs and have no connection with reality. In the 2nd style the decoration of a room was conceived holistically, while in the 3rd style each wall is an individual element. The observer's gaze does not focus on the overall scheme but on the various decorative elements, revealing a graphic elegance and an attention to detail absent in the other styles. Unlike the pictorialism of the 2nd style, the 3rd may be defined as a graphic style, in which the fine detail and the ornamental features blend with the rigid order of the wall's decorative scheme.

Another fundamental innovation, which was fully developed in the 4th style, is the importance given to the depiction of figures, mostly drawn from mythology. These are situated in the centre of the wall, as if in a picture, though this figurative work is always linked to the overall composition of the wall. The features described so far evolved gradually, and only become fully developed between the end of the 1st century BC and the first quarter of the 1st century AD. In the second quarter of this century, the order of this scheme gradually began to decline and eventually broke down. The tripartite scheme of the wall became less rigid and panels appeared with architectural elements seen from an angle, regaining a sense of perspective and ushering in the 4th style. The most beautiful wall decorations of the last of the styles include the *tablinum* of the House of Marcus Lucretius Fronto at Pompeii.

Other popular themes in the 3rd style, and again in the 4th, were pictures of villas by the sea and gardens, espe-

cially the enclosed garden (*hortus conclusus*), seen in perspective from a distance.

Another typical feature of 3rd style decoration is the Egyptian theme, which gained in popularity due to more frequent contacts with Egypt, after the country was conquered by Octavian. The simple linear style fitted in perfectly with the features of the 3rd style.

While the character and development of the wall paintings which can be classified in the first three decorative styles were, generally speaking, clearly defined, the "4th style" is much more complex and reveals a number of different features. It is sometimes difficult to know whether these distinctive features are due to natural development or contemporary artistic influences. What is certain is that the 4th style began to appear half way through the 1st century AD, and became the most eclectic of the decorations, owing to the blend of features from both the 3rd and 2nd styles. In the most elaborate versions, though there is a return to the theme of the "open" wall, with *trompe l'oeil* vistas, there are also extravagant and imaginary architectural elements typical of the 3rd style, though here in less detail. The composition usually comprises vast sections in colour covering the central part of the wall, almost like a carpet with ornate borders, also central panels with views or winged figures and narrow panels with architecture. In the upper part the theme of imaginary architecture is revisited, but without the coherence of the 2nd style. There is also greater use of central panels with mythological subjects, often inspired by Greek mythology. Another type of decoration which covers the whole wall with a scene, often inspired by theatre scenery, depicts well-known mythological characters or events. In some cases these appear to be scenes from plays, such as the one drawn from Euripides' *Iphigenia in Tauris*, painted on a wall in the house of Pinarius Ceriales in Pompeii. The new decorative themes of this style include large landscapes with scenes of hunting or wild animals fighting, painted on the end wall of the garden.

In conclusion, typical examples of the 4th style are complex and imaginary, with a wide range of colours, where the reality of architecture and the significance of the

*Frescoes in the 1st style in the House
of Sallust, Pompeii*

Fresco in the 2nd style from the Villa
of P. Fannius Synistor at Boscoreale.
Naples, Museo Archeologico Nazionale

*Fresco in the 3rd style from the Villa
of Agrippa Postumus at Boscoreale.
Naples, Museo Archeologico Nazionale*

24

Fresco in the 4th style from the
Palaestra at Herculaneum. Naples,
Museo Archeologico Nazionale

figures is often subordinated to the decoration, intended not so much as detailed representation but an overall décor. So far only a passing mention has been made of the painting of gardens and vernacular art. Garden painting, which became popular during the 3rd style and continued into the 4th, consisted of frescoes covering whole walls depicting luxuriant gardens with a wide range of flowers and shrubs, flying birds and decorative elements such as fountains and sculpture. Vernacular painting was more immediate and sketchy and not particularly accurate in its representation of scenes from daily life, showing divinities and historical events, such as the famous fight between the Pompeians and Nucerians which took place in the amphitheatre in Pompeii in 59 AD.

Garden statuary

Marisa Mastroroberto

It is only relatively recently that the location and function of statues in Pompeian gardens have been studied in the domestic environment. Painting was the main source of information to understand cultural trends and aesthetic taste in Roman garden design, where statuary did not seem to provide enough evidence to define the features of Pompeian art.

Interest in this subject began to emerge in the late 19th century, based on evidence from finds made during excavations. In 1894-1895, the House of the Vettii was discovered, with a garden containing statues. The continual and systematic removal of objects and works of art discovered in the houses excavated, which ended up in museums and private collections, was superseded by a growing interest in reconstructing the original environment using evidence from excavations and comparisons with paintings where the state of the finds gave little clue.

This new concept of archeology enabled some progress to be made in understanding the positioning of statues, which was probably very similar to the Roman custom when Pompeii was destroyed in 79 AD.

During the first decades of the 20th century research continued along these lines. Any statues found were often left *in situ* as, for example, in some Pompeian houses which are particularly famous for the location and design of the statues in the garden area, like the House of Loreius Tiburtinus and the House of the Adolescent.

The significance of statues found at Pompeii is mainly the way in which they were buried, which makes it possible to allocate a particular function to each piece, as part of the overall decorative scheme of the house, also to appraise a moment in time, 79 AD, which was crucial in the development of Roman society between the Augustan *princeps* and Domitian. The study of garden statuary over the 20th century usually classified the artefacts according to style.

In recent years Dwyer's approach to the problem has been, and still is, of great importance, based on his work on five Pompeian houses (House of M. Lucretius; VII 12, 17; VII 12, 22; House of Fortune; House of the Zither Player) using excavation accounts and archive materials. He rejected the classification according to type and used a topographical method instead. Each statue was given a precise location in the Pompeian house based on evidence from the site and by applying analytical criteria he attempted to identify the relationship between the functions of the various types of decoration and the different locations.

Some recent studies have mentioned the correlation between location and function in garden statuary, however there has not been a thorough study on a wider scale, to research small domestic statuary and its relationship with other elements. Inside the Roman house these elements comprise architecture, wall and floor decorations, and more generally the design of each house with the decorative or religious features.

The need to adopt a more "holistic" research method for Pompeii at the time of the eruption in 79 AD is now perceived more widely. Using new technology it is possible to study the interiors of Roman houses, their gardens and statues, as recent exhibitions on Pompeii have shown, with the theme of the garden given prominence, albeit in the context of the house.

The decorative scheme of the garden of a Roman house in the first century AD reflects complex cultural and religious attitudes to Nature, seen in the personification of divinities which represent it in various ways. Small statues in particular had a symbolic and associative function and embodied the fundamental elements of Roman religion which related to the propitiatory forces of Nature. This was manifested in gardens through the convergence (but also opposition) between Art and Nature, or Art and Culture.

Garden design, where a certain view of Nature was expressed, was based on the idea of a gift from the gods which man could embellish.

The progress from the early concept of the garden as a microcosm (the metaphor of a macrocosm) which changes from one culture to another, is expressed in Roman terms in the first century by the synthesis of Hellenistic cultural influence and the dual role – both religious and economic – which the garden assumed in the Roman tradition. This ambivalence is expressed in garden statuary, which shows features deriving from a variety

Pompeii, House of the Golden Cupids
in 1904

28

Pompeii, House of the Vettii in 1908

of different models, associated with Greek-inspired naturalism and the more rustic Italic tradition, brought together by the new fashion for the garden as a place of ostentation, with a proliferation of statues.

This attitude reflects a trend which was particularly fashionable starting in the Augustan period, with its roots in religion, closer to the tradition of the middle class which adapted the model of garden statuary used in the great villas. They felt the need, which was typical of their class, to surround themselves with apotropaic and propitiatory symbols linked to the forces of Nature and religious rites, conceived as a means of conflict with Nature. Most of the statues in Pompeian gardens are connected with Bacchus, with images of bacchantes and episodes from mythology.

The gardens are a stage set for the mythological world, full of symbols and divinities. These include small statues, *oscilla*, decorated tablets and theatre masks; solar clocks, the symbol of the daily and seasonal rhythms of Nature; herms, often two-sided, showing adolescent and bearded, a sign of time passing and the renewal of life. The theme of death, symbolised by the victory of one animal others, was already expressed by Nature in the complex world of Greek art; Nature was also depicted as a vast funerary garden under the aegis of a divinity.

Symbols of the Dionysian cult are the theatre masks, and images of Maenad and Silenus, the demons of Nature who are included among the bacchantes. Other symbols of this cult and its belief in immortality can be seen in the gryphon, the animal sacred to Apollo but also to Dionysus. Owing to the close links between the two divinities in the Delphic culture and at the same time the most representative funerary animal since time immemorial, this can be construed as a symbol of apotheosis.

Many motifs can be found on sarcophagi in Roman gardens, with an eschatological meaning, such as cupids with wreaths or cloven hooves, theatre masks, hunting scenes, sea monsters, and so on — all are widely documented in urban production in the 2nd century.

Bibliography

Döhl H. - Zanker P., in *Pompei 79*, Naples 1979, pp. 201-210; Dwyer E.J., *Pompeian Oscilla Collections*, in "RömMitt.", 88, 1981; Dwyer E.J., *Pompeian Domestic Sculpture. A study of five Pompeian Houses and their Contents*, Rome 1982; Grimal J.P., *I giardini di Roma antica*, Milan 1990 (it. trans.), I ed. 1943; Mastroroberto M., in *Domus Viridaria Horti Picti*, Naples 1992, exhibition catalogue, pp. 39-48; Franchi Dell'Orto L., in *Riscoprire Pompei*, Rome 1993, exhibition catalogue, p. 302; Jashemski W.F., *The Gardens of Pompeii, Herculanum and the Villas destroyed by Vesuvius*, I-II, New York 1993; Rebecchi F., in *Pompei. Abitare sotto il Vesuvio*, Ferrara 1996, pp. 163-167.

Catalogue

Paintings of gardens

Paintings of garden scenes on the walls of Pompeian houses start to appear in the 3rd style period. Unlike the complex "stage sets" of the 2nd style which used *trompe l'oeil* techniques to produce ambitious illusions, opening up the wall space to a place beyond, the years of Augustan age were marked by a change in fashion and taste.

In this new style, the picture space of the wall was divided into three sections based on a strict, formal scheme. The new Neo-Classical style was underlined by graceful architecture with slender columns to balance the formal decorative scheme.

The Augustan academic taste spread swiftly in the Arts via the new figurative language. The precepts of order, peace and justice were translated into a different vision of life, particularly as regards wall painting in houses. Examples of this less formal manner can be seen in paintings from Pompeii.

The idea of a peaceful, simple and orderly life required direct contact with Nature. In painting, natural elements overcame the constraints of domestic architecture, with the result that the artifice of Nature was brought right into the house on to the walls. Natural motifs were already present in Pompeian painting in landscapes and views, though these were idealised and imaginary. Garden painting became a form of representation which depicted flora and fauna naturally and intellectually, and provided decorative importance and centrality to the garden as part of the domestic environment. A great deal of love and care was lavished on the natural gardens of Roman houses towards the end of the Republic and during the Empire. In fact, gardening became a veritable hobby, which aimed to create artistic, even eccentric, effects in a natural environment using methods like topiary (*opus topiarum*). Garden painting imitated reality with many plants and flowers, birds in flight, fountains playing and beautiful marble sculptures in inner courtyards separated from the house by graceful structures with windows trellis work.

The painting of gardens at Pompeii can be divided into two phases. In the first, in the Julian-Claudian period, it was still influenced by the decorative scheme of the 3rd style. In this scheme a garden scene would appear on one of the sections of the wall with strict symmetrical organisation of the plants and decorative elements. The scene was viewed from the interior using *trompe l'oeil* techniques, where the walls were large windows opening out on to a garden on the fourth wall, with real gardens as well, for example, in the summer *triclinium*.

In the second phase, from 25 to 50 AD, the architectural elements of the previous scheme disappeared and the picture space of the central part of the painting was opened up. The garden scene covers the whole room, running from one wall to the next, viewed from the centre of the room as a kind of virtual reality. Examples of this type of painting can be found in the large basement room at the villa of Livia *ad gallinas albas* (with the white hens), a grand example of Roman garden painting which strong influenced provincial Pompeii. The walls were covered with a large garden surrounded by a low fence – a kind of Hellenistic paradise with luxuriant vegetation, fruit trees, rare plants and flowers, animated by birds in flight against a bright blue sky. (M.M.)

Bastet F.L. - De Vos M., *Proposta per una classificazione del terzo stile pompeiano*, Gravenhage 1979; Becatti G., in "EAA", VI, 1961, sv. *Ludius*, p. 276; Beyen H.G., in "EAA", VI, 1965, sv. *Pompeiani, stili*, pp. 356-366; Bianchi Bandinelli R., *Tradizione ellenistica e gusto romano nella pittura pompeiana*, in *Storicità dell'arte classica*, Florence 1950; Id., in "EAA", V, 1963, sv. *Paesaggio*, pp. 816-828; Id., *Roma. L'arte romana nel centro del potere*, Milan 1978, pp. 116-129; Borda M., *La pittura romana*, Rome 1959; Brigantini I. - Parise Badoni F., *Il quadro pompeiano nel suo contesto decorativo*, in "DdA", 1984, pp. 119-129;

Brigantini I. - De Vos M. - Parise Badoni F., *Pitture e pavimenti di Pompei*, Rome 1982, I-III, sv. *Giardino*, pp. 423-426; Conticello B., *Sull'evoluzione del giardino nell'antichità classica*, in "Rivista di Studi Pompeiani", 1993-1994, VI, pp. 7-13; Corlaita Scagliarini D., *Spazio e decorazione nella pittura pompeiana*, in "Palladio", 24-26, 1974, 1976, pp. 3-44; Dwyer E., *Pompeian Domestic Sculpture. A Study of five Pompeian Houses and their Contents*, Rome 1982; Gabriel M.M., *Livias' Garden Roma at Prima Porta*, New York 1955; Jashemski W.F., *The Gardens of Pompeii, Herculaneum and the Villas destroyed by Vesuvius*, New York 1993, II, pp. 313-404; Maiuri A., *Nuove pitture di giardi-*

no a Pompei, in "BdA", 37, 1952, pp. 5-12; Mastroroberto M., in *Domus Viridaria Horti Picti*, exhibition catalogue, Naples 1992, pp. 39-48; *Pompei. Pitture e Mosaici*, Rome 1990, II, pp. 1-137; *Riscoprire Pompei*, exhibition catalogue, Rome 1993, p. 302; pp. 328-334, n. 241; Rizzo G.E., *La pittura ellenistico-romana*, Rome 1929; Sampaolo V., in *Pompei* (ed. by F. Zevi), Naples 1991, p. 72; Zanker P., *Augusto e il potere delle immagini*, Turin 1989; Mastroroberto M., in *Pompeii. Picta fragmenta*, Turin 1997, pp. 61 *et sqq.*; Mastroroberto M., in *Pitture nella Reggia*, Naples 1999, pp. 76-77.

1. Wall with garden painting

Inv. no. 59467 a, b, c, d
Pompeii VI 17, 42
(House of the Gold Bracelet)
(a) 278 x 177 cm; (b) 278 x 192 cm;
(c) 121 x 83 x 43 cm; (d) 178 x 278 cm

This large painting covers the whole of the south wall of the summer *triclinium* in the so-called House of the Gold Bracelet, built on three levels overlooking the sea on the beautiful west side of the town. This room, discovered in 1979 (De Caro 1979, p. 178) during the extension of excavations on the lower terraces of this ambitious piece of architecture, opened out at the level of the garden where there was an adjoining room (the *oecus*), also splendidly decorated with garden paintings. The beautiful setting of the *triclinium* comprised tricliniar couches and a small water feature with fountains in the middle and water flowing from a fine *nymphaeum*, decorated in polychrome glass mosaics placed at the centre of the far wall (*Riscoprire Pompei*, 1993, pp. 318-324, no. 240). The water flowed from the centre of the *triclinium* down to a great fountain situated outside, near the room described here, into a natural garden which stood in front (*Pompei*, 1992, II, p. 72). This room, with its high vaulted ceiling, has retained *in situ* the original socle painted with imitation marble slabs, most of which are concealed by the brick tricliniar couches, covering four-fifths of the room. Above the high socle, at the guests' eye level, stood this imposing painting, which was probably one of a pair with a painting on the opposite side of the room, most of which, sadly, is now missing.

The decorative scheme used is based on a tripartite vertical division of the wall space. This division creates three sections: a central one (b), sub-divided into individual panels with a central niche (c), two lateral ones, one on the right (a) and one on the left (d), which have symmetrical composition and features.

The division into main sections is provided by the pilaster strips painted red which start from the jamb and proceed at regular intervals down to the corner at the bottom. On the first three pilaster strips starting from the right (the fourth is narrower and lacks decoration) are small ivory-coloured columns of the type used in 3rd style wall paintings to divide up the planes in large compositions (see Bastet - De Vos 1979, p. 75). These small columns, which support the vault and frame the central section are ridged and end at the top in small Ionic capitals, separated by a dado and a white fillet from the reddish brown cornice which runs along the entire wall like a trabeation. Half-way up the columns are two medallions with cupids on a black background (see Bastet - De Vos 1979, p. 94). On the left in bright colours and in a good state of preservation is an elegant cupid moving to the right with violet and yellow cloth draped rounds his hips, small green wings and holding a golden bowl. In the right-hand medallion, part of which is missing, another cupid is holding a box which opens to reveal tiny ivy leaves. The third small column, which closes the wall on the right, has different features: it is smooth and decorated with astragals which contain small facing Greek motifs on a yellow background (see Bastet - De Vos 1979, p. 96) ending in trailing vegetation. The central medallion, again a black background, contains part of a female figure moving towards the left in a pale blue dress and violet cloak, possibly a Maenad. The strong illumination of the small columns comes from the right, where the entrance to the room is situated.

The three sections defined by the pilaster strips are similar to stage scenery (the *trompe l'oeil* effect is lacking in the design of picture space, which is like a spectacular bas-relief) and show a scene of a garden framed in niches with a semi-circular tympanum (in the centre) and a triangular one (at the sides). The two architectural elements recur in a wall painting by the pool inside the *triclinium*, where a series of small marble niches shows the two types of tympanum alternating.

Light trellis structures surround the three sections: above with niches and a tympanum, and below (only in the two lateral ones) with a trellised socle, containing a sequence of screened and shaded niches which animate the perimeter of the parapet.

The central section contains a niche with a blue background (c), which obviously symbolises water and was probably made to protect a statue. The small temple, also covered with the same ridged structure, was connected to the semi-circular tympanum above by means of two small trellised columns, resulting in further divisions in the upper part of the central scheme. The idea of subdivision shows an ability to experiment with decoration. The three main sections show a large garden scene, designed as a single unit though each section has different features. The left-hand section (d) has marble sculptures in the foreground on the podium. In the centre stands a marble apsed vault used as a fountain; on the left is a statue of a man standing viewed in profile, dressed in the Egyptian manner in blue and yellow, wearing the traditional head-dress and a *uraeus*, holding the *ankh* – the gold symbol of life – in his lowered hand. To the right of the fountain is a large area which is damaged, which makes it impossible to see what it contained – probably the second statue of the pair facing the first.

36   Above, at the centre of the tympanum, a marble *oscillum* hangs of a bearded male head with curly hair, with parts of the face missing. The verdant vegetation of the garden is silhouetted against a blue background and contains many vertical elements. The vegetation in the garden consists of oleander, strawberry tree, laurel, viburnum, and other plants (for a more detailed list of the species and an interpretation of the symbolic value of the plants according to antiquity, see *Riscoprire Pompei* 1993, pp. 332 *et seqq*., no. 241). The vegetation is painted as if it were a drawing, with small highlights in colour representing the berries or flowers of the different species on each of the plants. The composition of the painting is in three sections with spaces allocated for the plants (for a description of the formal order and system of values expressed by aesthetic taste in the 3rd style, see Zanker 1989, pp. 297 *et seqq*.). This is more obvious in the central section (b) where the subdivision is accompanied by the vertical elements of the small attractive columns. A female mask hangs from the semi-circular tympanum (*oscillum*). In the right-hand section (a) the scheme is the same as the first and contains sculptures in the foreground in the Egyptian taste. On both sides is a pair of facing sphinxes in white marble standing on a base; in the centre is a rectangular marble slab on a small column which rises from an *omphalos* of palms (the slab shows the bull Apis inclined to the left). Above, suspended between the sloping sides of the tympanum, is a circular *oscillum* which has almost disappeared; at the sides two birds in flight connect the sky in the background with the vegetation below.

The entire garden scene is animated by the presence of many birds, both in flight and perching in different poses, in various colours according to the species to give colour to the scene. The picture recalls the wall paintings with garden scenes in rooms 8 and 12 of House I 9, 5, called the Floral Rooms or Orchard (*Pompei. Pitture*, 1990, pp. 1-137) which show a similar decoration, based on a strict division of the picture space. These features suggest that the painting dates back to the 3rd style in the Julian-Claudian period.   (M.M.)

Bibl.: *Orangerie italiana*, 1991, pp. 16-17; Mastroroberto, in *Pompeii. Picta fragmenta*, 1997, pp. 166-167, nos. 149-152; Mastroroberto, in *Pitture nella Reggia*, 1999, pp. 78-79, no. 43.

The Roman sea-side villa at the Contrada Sora near Torre del Greco

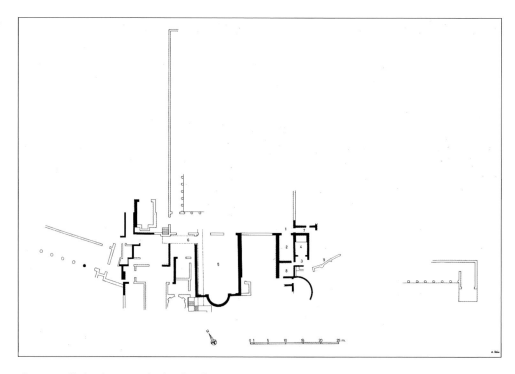

The great villa by the sea in the hamlet of Sora near Torre del Greco lies 3.6 km south-east of Herculaneum, between the cemetery and the town hall (the La Salle building) in this Vesuvian town. Some discoveries were made as early as the 17th century, when a relief with Orpheus, Hermes and Eurydice was found, now at the National Archeological Museum in Naples (inv. no. 6727). Surveys were carried out between 1733 and 1741, and a proper excavation was started, though it was abandoned in 1797 due to a series of political problems. The excavation was sponsored by the then crown prince, Francis I of Bourbon, and concentrated on the central nucleus of the villa round the atrium and an enormous reception room with an apse. The discoveries included a splendid copy of a Satyr by Praxiteles and two frescoes with theatrical themes, now at the Museum of Palermo. The small bronze statue of the fountain representing Hercules and the stag, also at Palermo, decorated the House of Sallust at Pompeii. Thorough excavations were not conducted until 1989, by the Soprintendenza Archeologica of Pompeii. During this work a number of beautifully frescoed rooms were found in the 3rd and 4th Pompeian styles, with floors covered in precious marble and mosaics; the area explored in the 18th century was also re-excavated, now in a sad state of repair. The recent excavations were temporarily suspended in 1992.

The villa, which looked out over the Bay of Naples, was over 200 metres long and had an enormous reception room, paved with marble tiles, measuring 12x19 m, facing north on to a peristyle with sides 60 m long. The identity of the owner of this luxury dwelling is not known, but he must have been a very important Roman aristocrat. The villa was built in the mid 1st century AD. and buried by the fatal eruption in 79 AD. Buildings stood here after the eruption as well, until about the 6th century AD.

Some panels from the upper area and ceiling of *cubiculum diurnum* no. 4 are on display in the exhibition, accompanied by a graphic reconstruction. The area measures 3.50x3.70 m with a niche placed at the far end, raised on a step measuring 2.70x1.90 m. The height after reconstruction is 4 m. On the east side there was a window looking out on to an open area, and the wide entrance was preceded by a vestibule. The floor was paved in precious marble tiles. The painting, in the early 4th style, has a brownish-purple socle (with signs of repair on the east side), with decorations in the niche of small lively parrots holding slender wreaths and swans, with rectangular panels on the other sides. On the side walls above the socle is a panel painting consisting of rectangular sections with small animals alternating with medallions of theatre masks, tripods and a deer. The ground is made up of large blue squares (in Egyptian blue, made at Puteoli with the name *Vestorianum*, after Cicero's banker friend), divided by reddish fascias decorated with pilaster strips with motifs of gilded vegetation, issuing from two oblique winged figures of Pegasus. The two lateral panels have horizontal red curving fascias on the long sides, and resemble luxurious hanging carpets with finely decorated borders. The frieze above, separated by a small white cornice, is 1.56 m. high and shows imaginary architectural motifs beneath an elegant cornice in stucco. The ceiling also had a blue background, and a fascia with a blue meander on white, while at the centre there was probably a panel with an attractive lozenge motif (see inv. no. 79558), which is included in

this exhibition. The soffit of the far niche, where the bed was situated, contained the painted panel which has been reconstructed (inv. no. 79547).

The high quality of the technique and the execution, with the use of much calcite in the preparatory layers, the sophistication and elegance of the subjects, suggests a commission at the very highest level. In fact, the frescoes can only be matched by the ones in the splendid villas of *Stabiae* and the most luxurious of the Pompeian residences.

(M.P.)

Bibliography

Pagano M., *La villa romana di contrada Sora a Torre del Greco*, in "CrErc", 21, 1991, pp. 149 *et seqq.*; Id., in "RivStPomp", VI, 1993-94, pp. 267 *et seqq.*; Pagano M. - Russo F. - Terrasi F. and Tuniz C., *Antropizzazione e attività vulcanica in alcuni siti archeologici di Torre del Greco (NA)*, in *Il sistema uomo-ambiente tra passato e presente*, edited by Albore Livadie C. and Ortolani F., Bari 1998, pp. 221-235.

2. Fresco

Inv. no. 79548
Torre del Greco, Villa Sora
Cubiculum diurnum no. 4.
100 x 384 cm

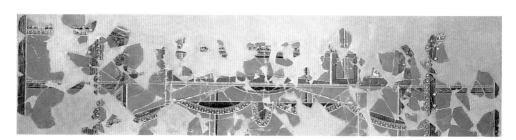

This frieze is on the west wall of the room. The elegant decoration consists of *trompe l'oeil* architecture with coffers and gilded cornices with *ovoli* supported by gilded candelabra and narrow columns on a blue ground. At the sides are motifs of bunches of grapes and myrtle and a panel with open leaves. In the centre two long golden *thyrsi* placed diagonally support drapery with fine gold borders against a dark red and brownish-purple background. The central niche had gilded borders with winged sphinxes facing a golden high footed tazza. The panels to the side of the central picture show moving leopards in front of small columns with comic theatrical masks. (M.P.)

3. Fresco

Inv. no. 79547
Torre del Greco, Villa Sora
Cubiculum diurnum no. 4.
125 x 273 cm

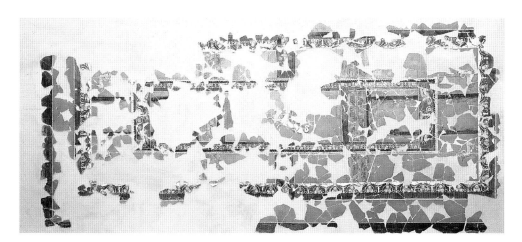

This is a reconstructed panel from the centre of the niche ceiling at the far end of the room. It has a gilded framed of ox sculls and palmettes among bunches of vegetation on a dark red ground. The two short sides show *trompe l'oeil* pergolas with fruit, at the base of which are pairs of centaurs holding a helm. In the centre is a rectangle, divided by two red fascias into three sections, with elegant borders of gilded vegetation on the long sides and two gryphons facing an urn among bunches of vegetation on the short sides. The centre of the blue rectangle probably contains the figure of Neptune, the upper half of which is missing, dressed in a purple tunic and golden mantle, driving a cart pulled by two sea goats.

In the middle of the two long sides are golden urns and an elaborate pedestal decorated with rams' heads. (M.P.)

4. Fresco

Inv. no. 79558
Torre del Greco, Villa Sora
Cubiculum diurnum no. 4.
70 x 80 cm

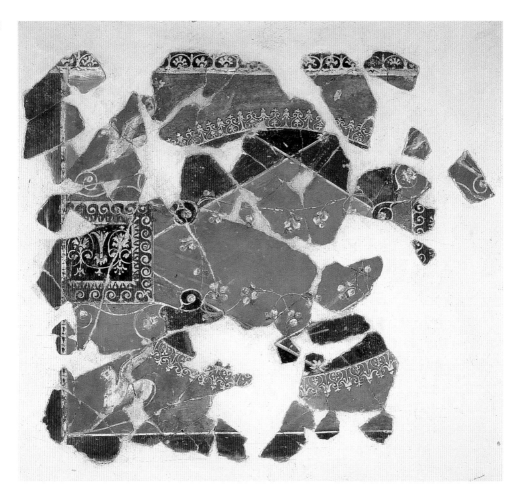

This rectangular panel with a blue ground and elegant gilded borders contains a lozenge motif in an ellipse, which was the central part of the ceiling in this room. The blue ground has a dark red frame decorated with elegant gilded borders with four rampant golden gryphons at the corners (only two remaining), surrounding a fine decoration with concentric squares, ellipses and lozenges with alternating fields of green, brownish-purple and blue with small golden plant and geometric motifs. In the central lozenge hang slender golden bunches of vegetation. (M.P.)

5. Fresco

Inv. no. 79557
Torre del Greco, Villa Sora
Cubiculum diurnum no. 4.
58 x 30 cm

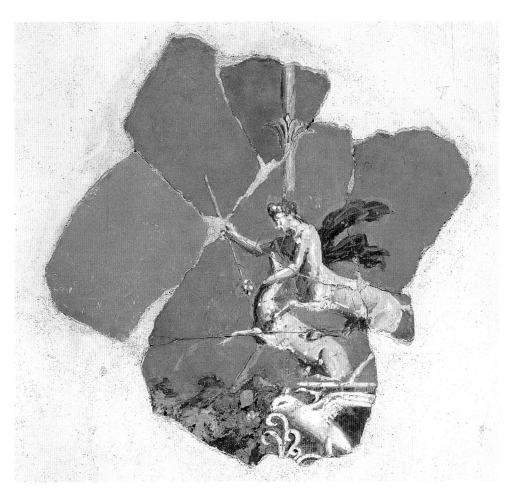

This interesting fragment of an *acroterium* is at the centre of east wall. A golden female centaur on a blue ground wearing a billowing chlamys is painted with white highlights, striking a deer with upturned head with her lance.

Beneath is an owl, perched on an *acroterium* with a palmette on a dark red ground. On the left is a band of vine leaves and above a golden candelabrum.

(M.P.)

Bibl.: *Pompeii. Picta fragmenta*, 1997, pp. 157 *et seqq.*; *Pitture nella Reggia*, 1999, pp. 43 *et seqq.*

6. Winged female figure

Inv. no. 41653
Pompeii VII 16, 22
(House of M. Fabius Rufus)
171 x 124 cm

44

This panel is made up of fragments and shows a life-size winged female figure in the foreground with her head turned three-quarters to the left in the form of a caryatid, supporting a corbel protruding from an architrave. The figure, adorned with gold jewellery (a necklace with rubies, earrings and a bracelet) holds in both hands a garland of ivy leaves decorated in the centre with a large bow of yellow fabric with purple stripes, which is loosely draped.

The pale flesh tones which are cleverly illuminated, as if to emphasise the statuary nature of the figure, and the soft hues of the wings, contrast with the bright colours of the architectural composition in the background against which the figure is silhouetted. This composition is a square panel surrounded by a border decorated with dolphins and palmettes, below which appears a flight of columns in perspective with a door in between. The iconography of the figure suggests a winged female figure at the House of the Epigrams, probably Season, in the manner of Abundance or Flora (see Moorman 1988, p. 162). It represents a goddess of vegetation, which stylistically and symbolically recalls a winged male figure in a fragment of decoration from the villa of P. Fannius Synistor at Boscoreale, now at the Louvre (see Tran Tam Tinh 1974, pp. 43-46, no. 22).

The exact wall from which the fragment from the first floor of the House of M. Fabius Rufus comes is not known. From comparison with similar paintings it probably belongs to the second decorative style, phase IIb (Beyen), featuring an architectural composition in the central part of the wall with winged female figures in the form of caryatids. The iconography suggests that the lower part of the figure, which is missing, would have been a herm or trailing vegetation.

Winged female figures similar to caryatids are frequent in second style Pompeian painting, for example, in the House of M. Caesius Blandus and in the House of Menander.   (C.C)

Bibl.: Cicirelli, in *Pompeii. Picta fragmenta*, 1997, p. 76, no. 6; Cicirelli, in *Pitture nella Reggia*, 1999, p. 84, no. 46.

7. Marriage of Mars-Alexander and Aphrodite-Roxana

Inv. no. 41657
Pompeii VI 17, 42
(House of the Gold Bracelet)
155 x 143 cm

46 Originally, the picture discussed here was in the centre of a black wall. Reconstructed from fragments, it is surrounded by a narrow reddish-brown border.

The picture space is almost entirely taken up by the characters in the scene. On the left is the dominating figure of a young hero, depicted in a statuary pose, standing on his left leg which supports all his weight, painted in a reddish tone, with his right leg slightly bent. He is holding up his right arm and clasps a long pole which stands almost vertical, the point touching the ground in front of his right foot, his left arm clutching the hilt of a sword suspended from a baldric. He wears a reddish-brown chlamys, loosely fastened and draped over the chest, falling from his shoulders to his knees, thus revealing his impressive naked body.

His head is turned slightly to the left, his hair is untidy and his expression intense, eager and determined.

Behind the young man in the duller shades usually used for backgrounds is a warrior dressed in the oriental style wearing a head-dress in yellow fabric, a short tunic and tight-fitting stockings. He holds a round shield in his left hand and a lance in his right. On the right of the picture is a girl, shown full face, with her left leg crossed and her right elbow leaning on a small column in the typical pose of Aphrodite. Her right hand is placed on her hip and on her left arm rests a sceptre. She wears a pale yellow chiton, the upper part almost transparent, which has slipped down her left shoulder; a blue mantle is draped over her back and is fastened at the front, falling into folds. Her head is turned slightly to her right, and her wavy hair frames her face, drawn back and fastened at the neck. She wears a precious gold and pearl diadem, pearl earrings and bracelets on both wrists. At her feet is a Chalcidian helmet with a pink and white plume. Behind the woman is a typical cupid, with strong highlighting of the skin, looking up at the girl. In his left hand he holds a bow and in the right clasps an enormous round shield. Behind the group is a pavilion with columns above which a fragment of sky can be seen. Together with a group of trees in the left-hand corner, these are the main elements in the landscape where the historical event is set of the marriage of Alexander the Great and Roxana or Statira. This has been transformed by a process of assimilation from the mythical-heroic theme of the marriage of Mars and Venus, which is common in Pompeian painting. The young man shows similarities with the well-known iconography of Alexander with his lance and shows the imperious glance and untidy hair characteristic of his face in the famous mosaic in the House of the Faun at Pompeii, a figure which has been identified as Alexander the Great. This identification is evident in the picture discussed here because of the Persian standing behind the hero, whose nationality is clear from the costume he is wearing. The female figure can be identified by her relation to Alexander (clearly an amorous one) and suggests Roxana, the daughter of Oxyartes, Satrap of Bactra, whom Alexander married in 327 (see Lagi De Caro 1988, pp. 75-88). This marriage of love was also painted in the famous painting by Aetion (Luciano, *Herodotus, sive Aetion*, 211, 4-6) which inspired many an artist and whose works may include the prototype from which the Pompeian painting derives. Recently, interpreting the attribute of the young woman as a royal sceptre, Moreno has identified her as Statira, daughter of Darius III, who was married at Susa in 324. This identification is justified by the presence of the escort in typical Persian costume, which was not re-introduced by Alexander until 324 (see *Alessandro Magno*, 1995, p. 66).

This painting comes from the *triclinium* (Room 20) on the second floor of the house to the north of M. Fabius Rufus, called the House of the Gold Bracelet. It was part of the decoration of the south wall, symmetrical to the north wall and in a better state of conservation, which can be dated to the early 4th style. From the central part is a main panel showing an intoxicated Dionysus between a Maenad and Silenus, one of a pair with the painting discussed here on the opposite wall, also two medallions, one with a Maenad and a Satyr, the other with a girl and an older woman (see inv. 20544/cat. no. 19). This decorative scheme seems to have an erotic theme, admirably expressed by an artistic adaptation of this well-known historical event.   (C.C.)

Bibl.: *Alessandro Magno*, 1995, p. 66 with previous bibliography; Cicirelli, in *Pompeii. Picta fragmenta*, 1997, pp. 130-131, no. 82; Cicirelli, in *Pitture nella Reggia*, 1999, p. 70, no. 37.

8. Dionysus and Ariadne

Inv. no. 41658
Pompeii VI 17, 42
(House of the Gold Bracelet)
216 x 129 cm

Removed from the north wall of Room 5 of the so-called House of the Gold Bracelet in the west Insula in 1980, this painting is set in part of the original wall. The black walls of this large vaulted room, decorated in a scheme typical of the early 4th style, contained two large paintings placed side by side, showing two famous couples from classical mythology: Mars and Venus on one side and Dionysus and Ariadne on the opposite side. Originally part of the grandiose decoration in the last Pompeian style, the panel retains some of the upper frieze in a reddish-brown colour, completed at the base by a dentellated cornice showing a fine series of yellow gryphons with blue wings, facing each other and alternating with imaginary human figures carrying salvers. A bearded mask with a gold crown is the central theme and volutes lead off from the lower bodies of mythical winged monsters. The volutes consist of spiralling vegetation terminating in little roses and buds, and revisit a typical motif of the proto-imperial figurative repertory (see Bastet - De Vos, 1979, p. 21).

Below the frieze on the wall painted black is the upper fascia of the border showing vine leaves intertwined with ivy and dotted with red and yellow corymbs which surrounded the main scene. This has a red frame with a white external fillet separating it from the black wall. Using varied and vivid colours this painting shows the figures of Dionysus and Ariadne in the foreground, with Silenus behind them, carefully observing the scene. Right in front is a small labyrinth made of bricks. In the background, painted in soft tones of grey and green, is a creek at the foot of a rocky arid landscape, represented by a few bare bushes. In the bay in the upper

right hand corner is the ship of Theseus, its prow facing the open sea as it leaves the island.

The episode depicted in this painting follows the desertion of Ariadne at Naxos and the arrival of Dionysus, who is attracted by the girl's beauty. The god is captured in a moment of tender love, reclining on a rock with his right arm raised and bent, and a splendid crown on his head of vine leaves and corymbs, his thyrsus beside him resting against the rock. His red chlamys with a bright blue border is draped over his raised arm and falls to his hips. His pose, turned slightly to the left is in movement, suggested by the frontal depiction of his left leg and the rotation of his face towards the girl, in a slight inclination to the right of the composition, as if his infatuated gaze were the real focus of the scene. His left arm touches the breast of Ariadne on the right of the painting, who is naked and adorned only with two gold pendant earrings, trying to cover her hips with the green-blue mantle which blows behind her, billowing in the mystic wind of theophany. A variation of the theme, the epiphany of Dionysus and a slumbering Ariadne, appears in some famous Pompeian paintings. From the nearby house of Fabius Rufus in the *Insula Occidentalis* is a pair of panels in cameo glass from the Julian-Claudian period (see Maiuri 1961, p. 18 *et seqq.* Pl. 2) one of which shows this scene. The theme of the billowing mantle can be found in several paintings, including the famous one at the House of the Zither Player (I 4, 25) where Dionysus discovers Ariadne sleeping, but he is the one whose robe is billowing in the divine breeze. As regards the theme of the seduction of the girl, which is typical in Dionysian contexts, similar treatment can be found in a painting of a satyr embracing Ariadne from the House of L. Caecilius Jucundus (V 1, 26). The composition focuses on the right-hand side, guiding the observer's gaze towards the sensual capitulation, emphasised by the long diagonal line of the *thyrsus*. The balance of the composition is restored by the expedient of the figure of Silenus on the left emerging from the rock. With long white beard, beaky nose, fat belly, dark skin and long red goat-like ears the old satyr holds a tambourine with one hand and a *thyrsus* in the other, in the opposite direction to the main axis of the composition. The style of the painting is rather theatrical and derives from a number of features. These include the composition based on the movement of figures in different directions, the spatial dimension which does not foreshorten the foreground elements but puts them into perspective with a clever use of light and shade, the correct anatomical proportions, the rapid lively brushstrokes and the modelling of the volumes obtained with a skilful use of the rich palette. (M.M.)

Bibl.: *Pompei*, 1992, p. 258; *Pompei. Pitture*, VII, 1996, pp. 80-83; Mastroroberto, in *Pompeii. Picta fragmenta*, 1997, pp. 131-133, no. 83; Mastroroberto, in *Pitture nella Reggia*, 1999, p. 71, no. 38.

The country villa of "Asellius" in the Vesuvian countryside

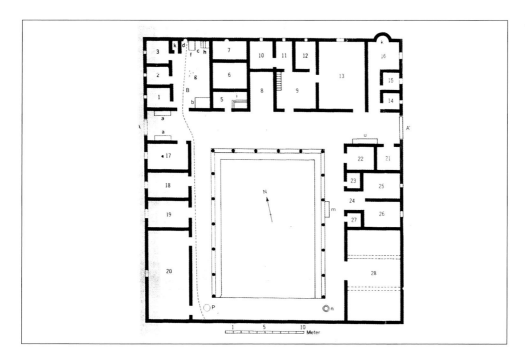

Between the late 19th and early 20th century many excavations were conducted in the Vesuvian countryside in search of the rural and rustic residential architecture which was so frequent in classical times on the fertile land between Vesuvius and the Lattari mountains.

These excavations, conducted privately with the ministerial authorisation required by law at the time, brought to light a large number of villas, which have provided valuable information in terms of history of art, architecture, farming methods and the economy of the Roman world. All these sites, usually excavated to obtain artefacts rather than for scientific reasons, were immediately covered over again, sometimes even while the excavations were being conducted. Consequently, little remains of these sites except for the brief reports written about them by the archeologists who directed the work on behalf of the authorities, and twenty-five per cent of the finds, which belong to the State by law.

One of these sites is the "Villa of Asellius", named after a bronze seal which bears the inscription: *Thalli Asel(li) pro(curatoris)*, meaning "(seal) of Thallus, administrator of Asellius", or *Thalli Asel(li) Pro(culi)* meaning "Thallus (administrator) of Asellius Proculus". Located on a site which was difficult to identify on a hill to the north of Pompeii, now in the Boscoreale area, the villa was discovered between February 1903 and November 1904 on the De Martino land by Vincenzo De Prisco, who had made several other interesting finds in the area.

This complex, unlike other rustic sites known at the time in this hilly agricultural area, does not appear to have facilities to make or store produce like wine and oil, and would therefore seem to be for residential purposes. The building contains large reception rooms (13 and 20), *triclinia* (15, 18), *cubicula* (11, 12, 25, 26) an *exedra* (8), a *venereum* (19) and baths, only part of which were in use (5, 6, 7). There were also rooms for practical purposes (B, 1, 2, 3, 4), storage areas such as *apothecae* (10, 14, 27),

50 two cells at the entrances (17 and 21), and other rooms whose function is unclear. The rooms were arranged in an orderly manner round a large garden, with a colonnade on three sides consisting of Doric columns connected by a low *pluteus* closed off at the south end by a wall.

The villa was probably built in the 1st century BC, judging from some wall paintings which can be attributed to the 2nd style that were left in situ and covered over. The villa was damaged during the AD 62 earthquake, and repairs and alterations to several rooms followed at a later date. Buried by the eruption in 79 AD, an event in which five of the inhabitants were killed, the villa was partially excavated in antiquity, as evidenced by the traces left in the strata and confirmed by the small number of objects found during the excavation.

De Prisco removed numerous panels containing fine frescoes in the 2nd and 4th style which decorated the main rooms, some of which now belong to the State. Five belonged to the walls of Room 16, whose function is unknown, which was decorated with pictures in the 4th style with a yellow background and showed *trompe l'oeil* architecture and festoons. The large panels which decorated the south and east walls contained winged male figures (cupids) and a female one (*psyche)* holding various objects (cat. nos. 10-13). The north wall contained a niche with two medallions in the centre depicting the bust of a young woman with a cupid at her shoulder, while the vault was decorated with flowers, birds, faces of characters from the Dionysian cult and objects associated with it. At the sides of the niche were two small green tigers and two symmetrical panels, one already in poor condition at the time of the excavation, the other now conserved (cat. no. 16).

The *exedra* (Room 8) had a yellow background. The walls were divided at the top and the bottom by red fascias with candelabra or *trompe l'oeil* architecture. On the east and west walls, beneath the floral festoons, were two small pictures with a red frame, one containing peacocks (cat. no. 9), the other a bird pecking at fruit. In the centre of the north wall was a picture of Venus Pompeiana, with helm and sceptre, accompanied by a figure holding a mirror and a man on a boat on the right, with a bird with two cherries in its beak on the left.

Another sacred image was painted in a niche in Room 22, representing a half-naked Bacchus making a sacrifice at an altar with two sheep nearby, while on the right of the god stands a large basket full of grapes.

Room 18 was probably a *triclinium*, with a 4th style painting on the north and south walls, while the west wall had no decoration and may have been covered by drapes; the east wall was found in a very poor state. The painted walls had a tripartite scheme with a socle showing simple floral motifs. The central part consisted of three red panels separated by *trompe l'oeil* architecture, which continued on the upper part with a white background. The architectural views depicted a bundle of fish and a peacock. In the centre of the panels and the corresponding parts of the frieze above were two rows of figures: to the north Spring, Bacchus and Summer, beneath a maenad, a satyr seated on a wineskin (cat. no. 15), and Silenus; to the south Autumn, Apollo and Winter, beneath a priestess, a muse and a devotee making a sacrifice (cat. no. 14).   (G.S.)

Bibliography

On rustic residential architecture north of Pompeii, Casale A. - Bianco A., *Primo contributo alla topografia del suburbio pompeiano*, in "Antiqua", suppl. no. 15, Oct.-Dec. 1979, pp. 27-56.
On the Villa of Asellius: Della Corte M., *La "villa rustica Aselli" esplorata dall'on. sig. Vincenzo De Prisco nel fondo De Martino in contrada Pisanella (Com. di Boscoreale) negli anni 1903-1904*, in "Notizie degli Scavi", 1921, pp. 426-35; Stefani G., in *Pompeii. Picta fragmenta. Decorazioni parietali dalle città sepolte*, exhibition catalogue Yokohama-Fukuoka 12 April - 31 August 1997, pp. 68-70; Stefani G., *Boscoreale: la Villa di Asellius e le sue pitture*, in "Rivista di Studi Pompeiani", IX, 1998, pp. 41-62; Stefani G., *Villa rustica detta di Asellius, agro pompeiano*, in *Pitture nella Reggia dalle città sepolte. Affreschi antichi da Pompei, Stabiae, Ercolano*, exhibition catalogue, Portici 12 March-4 July 1999, pp. 51-58.
For the peacock fresco, previously part of the Mildenberg Collection, *Tierbilder aus Vier Jahrtausenden. Antiken der Sammlung Mildenberg*, exhibition catalogue, Berlin 1983, p. 171 and Pl. on p. 180.

9. Peacock

Inv. no. 81656
"Agro Pompeiano" (Vesuvian
countryside near Pompeii),
Villa of Asellius, Room 8, east wall
48.5 x 30.3 cm

On the yellow wall is a small painting with a red frame and white fillet showing a peacock facing left, painted in green and red tones, standing on a white line with three small plants.
The peacock motif is very common in Pompeian wall painting, both as part of architectural scenes, as an isolated figure in the central panels, or in actual paintings as in this case. A similar example with a green frame can be found at a house in Pompeii (I 12, 11 Room 9, see *Pompei. Pitture*, 1990, II, p. 821) and in more complex depictions of still lifes (I 10, 10 Room 4) or in elaborate garden scenes (I 11, 6 *viridarium* 8). (G.S.)

10. Cupid

Inv. no. 15108
"Agro Pompeiano" (Vesuvian
countryside near Pompeii),
Villa of Asellius, Room 16,
probably east wall
27 x 27 cm

52

A small cupid is shown in flight on a dark yellow background. He is facing the front, with his right leg slightly bent, and his right arm at his side. His left arm is raised and he holds an elongated object in his hand, probably a *patera* with offerings. He is naked with just a green veil billowing out at the side over his left arm, twisting round his leg. The profile of the figure is painted dark pink while the flesh tones are pale pink with chiaroscuro. The attribute held in the left hand and the wings are dark pink, almost brown in colour.   (G.S.)

11. Cupid

Inv. no. 15107
"Agro Pompeiano" (Vesuvian
countryside near Pompeii),
Villa of Asellius, Room 16, east wall
29 x 30.5 cm

A small cupid is shown in flight against a dark yellow ground. The figure, with curly hair and possibly wearing a wreath, is flying to the right with legs crossed and his head turned in the opposite direction. Naked, with a green veil billowing at this side, suspended from his left arm he holds a shepherd's crook (*pedum*) in his right hand with his right arm raised, while his left arm is folded over his breast and he clasps a *syrinx*, another bucolic symbol. The wings, profile and details of the figure are dark pink, almost brown in colour, while the body is a pale pink with chiaroscuro effects, also present on the *pedum* and the *syrinx*.   (G.S.)

12. Cupid

Inv. no. 15111
"Agro Pompeiano" (Vesuvian
countryside near Pompeii),
Villa of Asellius, Room 16, south wall
41 x 28.5 cm

54   A small cupid is in flight against a dark
yellow background. He is facing the
front with his left leg slightly retracted
and glances to the right, with a wreath
of vegetation on his curly locks.
Completely naked, his right arm is
raised and he holds a *rhyton* (a vase) in
his hand, while his left arm is lowered
and he holds a pail. The wings, profile
and details of the figure are painted dark
pink, almost brown; the flesh is pale
pink, with chiaroscuro effects. The
rhyton and pail are grey with white
highlights to give a silvery sheen.   (G.S.)

13. Winged female figure

Inv. no. 15110
"Agro Pompeiano" (Vesuvian
countryside near Pompeii),
Villa of Asellius, Room 16,
probably on the east wall
35.6 x 39.5 cm

A small winged female figure (*psyche*)
in flight is shown on a dark yellow
ground facing the front. Her left leg is
slightly in profile, her hair is curly
probably with a wreath and her head is
turned to the right. She wears a long
thin tunic, tied round the waist falling
into transparent folds around her
ankles; with both arms she holds a long
green object, at a slight angle, probably
a large bronze salver (*lanx*). The wings,
profile and details of the figure are a
dark shade of pink, while the bare skin
and the tunic are pale pink, picked out
with highlights. The figure was probably
wrongly identified by Della Corte as a
cupid with a gladius, on the east wall,
while a similar figure described by him
on the south wall holding a bow and
arrow was left in situ.
Flying or moving figures (cupids,
psychai, victories, satyrs, maenads,
adolescents and female dancers) with
various poses and attributes, alone or in
pairs, frequently appear in the centre of
panels in the middle of walls decorated
in 3rd and particularly 4th style in
Pompeian houses.   (G.S.)

14. Male figure making a sacrifice

Inv. no. 41679
"Agro Pompeiano" (Vesuvian
countryside near Pompeii),
Villa of Asellius, Room 18,
south wall
79.5 x 58.5 cm

56   A man stands on a white background
facing the front. He is bald or his head is
shaved and he wears a wreath. He is
turning slightly to the right and wears just
a dark yellow mantle which reveals his
right arm, part of his breast and his lower
legs. He wears shoes on his feet. In his
right hand he clasps a small yellow vase, a
kantharos, holding it away from his body.
A patch of yellow indicates the ground
where the man is standing. The naked
parts of the body are painted dark red.
The picture is framed above and on the
left by a narrow dark red cornice with
double white fillet and an outer
decorated border, consisting of a yellow
band outlined in reddish purple and
green and decorated with a row of
opposing triangles. On the right is a
vertical band in reddish purple with
yellow borders. The lower frame is poorly
conserved, and consists of a simple
fascia in two shades of yellow, with a
reddish purple border.
The small metal *kantharos* and wreath
on his head denote a devotee preparing
to make a sacred offering to a divinity
which could be Apollo, shown in the
centre of the lower part of the wall, while
this panel is situated at the right-hand
edge of the upper part.   (G.S.)

15. Satyr on a wineskin

Inv. no. 56301
"Agro Pompeiano" (Vesuvian
countryside near Pompeii),
Villa of Asellius, Room 18,
north wall
110 x 111 cm

A satyr is seated in profile on a white
background, his left elbow leaning on a
wineskin. He wears a small wreath on
his head and is holding a *kantharos* in
his right hand. The figure wears an
animal skin round his hips revealing a
curly tail; he is inside a small building
with a coffered ceiling from which hang
a shield and two festoons.
This panel was the central part of the
upper decoration of the north wall of
this room and at the sides were the
figures of a maenad and a bearded
Silenus, both bacchantes associated with
the divinity shown in the centre of the
lower wall. This theme has similarities
with other Pompeian paintings, for
example, a picture at the House of
Ganymede (VII 13, 4) (see Reinach
1922, p. 121, 8), with the same depiction
of a seated satyr in profile with a
kantharos, but in a natural setting. This
painting, like the rest of the decoration
in this room, is in the 4th style.   (G.S.)

16. Fragment with relief

Inv. no. 15109
"Agro Pompeiano" (Vesuvian
countryside near Pompeii),
Villa of Asellius, Room 16,
north wall
31.5 x 36.8 cm

A rectangular panel with a red frame bordered in white stands against a yellow ground on a wall divided up by two green vertical bands with a white border. The panel has a black ground and shows several figures fighting, including warriors with helmets, shields, swords and axes, while in the centre a soldier on horseback is fighting a man on foot, with a soldier falling to his knees behind them. The figures are painted grey and white, and arranged around a base line indicating the battlefield. Above the panel is a high centrepiece, and the wall is decorated with diagonal motifs simulating wicker-work. The motifs include an unclear image, a round glass flask with a narrow neck and elaborate handle, and a small banner suspended from the centrepiece. This ornament and its contents are painted brown and grey with highlights. The panel is interesting as it enables the wall decoration to be reconstructed. The presence of *trompe l'oeil* forms on the wall, a motif used quite often in 2nd style wall paintings, is rare in the 4th style (see Moormann 1988, pp. 37-39), and similar to contemporary friezes in stucco. The same effect could be obtained by inserting real marble reliefs into the wall, as in the peristyle at the House of the Golden Cupids at Pompeii (VI 16, 7). These elements reveal the taste of this period, which was highly ornate. (G.S.)

The House of the Cryptoporticus

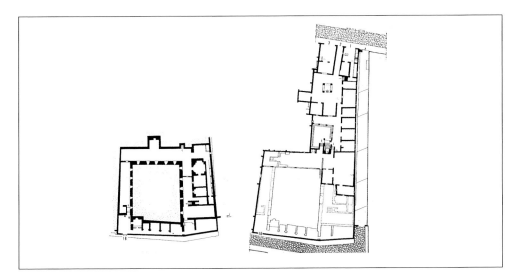

In July 1910 Vittorio Spinazzola, a brilliant Neapolitan scholar, became director of excavations at Pompeii. From 1911 until 1923 he was responsible for a series of large-scale excavations, intending to bring to light the whole of Via dell'Abbondanza, the main street in Pompeii, and by so doing to connect the area of the Forum with the Amphitheatre built just behind the defensive walls. The operation was an unexpected success and revealed aspects of Pompeii hitherto virtually unknown. The town appeared colourful and lively with its vivid shop signs, paintings of divinities in the popular taste and electoral propaganda painted on the walls of houses. The careful organisation of the excavations made it possible to reconstruct the upper storeys of the buildings more accurately, which apparently were embellished with balconies, loggias and verandas, opening out over the busiest street in town.

The only drawback was that as the excavations hardly ever went further than the façades it was difficult to imagine exactly how the whole street appeared. However, some important residences were brought to light including the House of the Cryptoporticus, which contained sophisticated decorations, some in stucco and some painted.

Originally, the House of the Cryptoporticus and the ad-joining House of the *Sacellus Iliacus* formed a single building, which underwent a radical transformation after severe damage suffered in the earthquake of 62 AD and was divided into two houses.

This house, which was still being renovated in 79 AD, consists of an atrium leading to a small peristyle at the bottom of which is a staircase up to a summer *triclinium* with a large portico overlooking a garden, possibly used as a public meeting place.

Another small staircase by the first leads down to the cryptoporticus, part of which was used in the latter years of the building as a cellar for the summer *triclinium* upstairs, though in the cryptoporticus the decorative stucco and paintings were untouched.

The original appearance of this part of the building in Samnite times was probably a portico surrounding a rectangular-shaped garden. In Roman times it was turned into a basement area (*cryptoporticus*) by raising the level of the garden to the height of the small embrasures, providing it with a small private bath, with *apodyterium*, *tepidarium*, *calidarium* and *frigidarium*.

Behind the bath was a large reception room (*oecus*) with a ceiling decorated in stucco from which frescoes in the 2nd style were removed (cat. no. 17). (E.D.C.)

17. Second style decoration

Inv. nos. 59468 (north wall),
59469 a-b-c-d (south wall)
Pompeii I 6, 2
(House of the Cryptoporticus)
210 x 205 cm (north wall), 210 x 960 cm
(south wall)

The painted decoration in the room (see Spinazzola 1953, I, pp. 496 *et seqq.*) in the lower part shows a plinth and a low podium with trailing flowers and vegetation. Above this is an elegant composition with male and female herms on pedestals which support the corbels of a coffered ceiling, with alternating masks and glass vases suspended in front. The decoration terminates in a cornice made of stucco representing bulls alternating with acanthus leaves. The vault of the ceiling rises from the cornice. In the middle ground behind the herms is a wall painted yellow, imitating marble, and above it a Doric frieze and an Ionic column. A narrow floral garland is looped between the herms surrounded by a trailing vegetation which serves as a perch for small birds. The herms are purple in colour and seen in profile, holding musical instruments such as the lyre, the kettle-drum, the double flute, pan-pipes and objects such as a *patera* and a cornucopia. The section between the bust and the pedestal is naked in the male herms and covered by a veil in the females. Behind the herms, above the Ionic cornice of the wall is a frieze with *pinakes* (paintings protected by projecting wooden frames with four leaves) depicting still-lifes or symbolic scenes alluding to Dionysian mysteries. The only remaining fragment of painting on the north wall of the room shows a *pinax* of Ariadne being carried on a cart, perhaps to her wedding, preceded by a girl playing the double

flute. The south wall, in a better state of conservation, shows a sequence of images: an unidentifiable landscape with architecture; reclining satyrs and maenads banqueting in the *triclinium*; a still life with cockerel, basket of fruit and towel; Charon on a boat accompanied by two female figures in conversation with a seated philosopher; Victory with a palm branch and shield with a lateral seated female figure and a boy standing on the right holding a tablet, with a female figure in the middle ground holding a flabellus. The whole of the lower part of the south wall and a fragment of the north wall are covered with graffiti suggesting hunting scenes in the amphitheatre.

The painting in the *oecus*, which belongs to the last phase of the second style, is usually dated between 40 and 20 BC (Barbet 1985, pp. 40-41; Ling 1991, pp. 32-33).

The frescoes in the *oecus* of the House of the Cryptoporticus illustrate a particular composition theme of the second style which favours imposing herms facing a single wall with seven lively figures (Moorman 1988, pp. 13-18). Two more interesting examples of this type of decoration can be found in the bath of the House of Menander (*Pompei. Pitture*, 1990, II, p. 378) and in the *oecus* of House VII I, 40 (*Pitture e Pavimenti*, 1986, III, p. 47) while the decoration of the *tablinum* in House VII 2, 20 with herms placed between columns (*Italienische Reise*, 1989, p. 192, no. 46) belongs to an earlier period. The series of *pinakes*, which are of particularly high

quality, painted on the upper part of the wall show different subjects, not necessarily associated with the use of the room for reception or banquets (Spinazzola 1953, I, pp. 503-531). In addition to the three *pinakes* with still lifes (most of the *pinax* on the east wall has been lost and is not on display) four more *pinakes* have been preserved with symbolic subjects or scenes linked to Dionysian myths. The north wall shows the marriage of Ariadne and the south wall has a sequence of still-lifes, a group of satyrs at a banquet, a funeral scene signifying that death should not frighten the bacchantes, and finally a seated follower to whom Victory shows a tablet with the triumphs of Dionysus. It has been suggested by Ragghianti that the frescoes in the *oecus* may be the work of a great Pompeian artist called the Master of the Cryptoporticus, who was an expert in the use of colour and produced majestic paintings. Ragghianti also believes the same artist was responsible for the paintings in the small atrium of the bath in the House of Menander and the painting with Hercules and Omphale in the House of M. Lucretius Stabia (Ragghianti 1963, pp. 60-63). (E.D.C.)

Bibl.: Spinazzola 1953, I, pp. 437 *et seqq.*; *Pitture e Pavimenti*, 1981, I, pp. 22-25; *Pompei. Pitture*, 1990, I, pp. 255-273; De Carolis, in *Pompeii. Picta Fragmenta*, 1997, pp. 75-76, nos. 1-5; De Carolis, in *Pitture nella Reggia*, 1999, pp. 81-82, no. 44

18. Female bust

Inv. no. 16594
Pompeii II 3, 3
(House of Venus in a Shell)
Sides 41 x 40 cm

This small picture, which was removed from a frescoed wall, shows a young woman with bands of wavy hair playing a lyre. She is looking at the instrument with her head tilted back and concentrating on her music.

This version is similar to paintings of Muses playing musical instruments, but it does not have the same features and is more likely to be a portrait of a woman, which is particularly expressive.   (L.F.)

Bibl.: Bellezza 1992, p. 107; *Neapolis* 1994, pp. 135-136; Fergola, in *Pompeii. Picta Fragmenta*, 1997, p. 99, no. 43; Fergola, in *Pitture nella Reggia*, 1999, p. 91, no. 52.

19. Medallion with couple

Inv. no. 20544
Pompeii VI 17, 42
(House of the Gold Bracelet)
43 x 41 cm

A panel detached from a black wall bears a medallion bordered with a double cornice of green leaves; the pink ground shows the half busts of a young woman, also in shades of pink, and an old woman behind her. The young woman is painted full face with her head leaning back slightly to the right. She wears a wreath of vegetation on her blond curly hair, which is parted down the middle. Her face is painted in soft flesh tones and her features are regular, while her fixed, absent gaze denotes concern and trepidation, a state of mind emphasised by her eyes which are wide open and her parted lips. Her upper body is covered in a transparent veil highlighted in white with fine

64 brushstrokes. Behind the young woman is the bust of an old woman looking closely at the perturbed young woman. She wears a green veil revealing some hair which has slipped out on to her wrinkled brow. The pink chiton she wears is slightly darker than the flesh tones of her face.

The old woman is probably the nurse, the wise counsellor, who would have the task of instructing the young woman about love, judging from the erotic nature of the theme dominating the painting in the room where this medallion would have been situated. The fresco comes from a large *triclinium* with a vaulted ceiling (Room 20) on the second floor of the house to the north of M. Fabius Rufus, usually called the House of the Gold Bracelet, built on three storeys by the city walls with a view over the Sarno valley and the sea. It belonged to the decoration of the north wall, which is the best preserved and the most important example.

This sophisticated painting in the early fourth style has a bipartite composition. The black socle consists of rectangular panels alternating with square sections with symmetrical repetition of the motifs at the sides of the central panel with a situla hanging from garlands, and a peacock. The central part features three large black squares alternating with architectural views. The central square contains the main picture showing a drunken Dionysus between a Maenad and Silenus, while the lateral ones, surrounded by ornate borders with heart-shaped elements have two central medallions: the one on the left with Maenads and Satyrs, the one on the right with the young woman and the old lady already described. Above the central part runs a red frieze with a decoration of vegetation corresponding to the lateral squares in the central part with grotesque motifs placed on the same axis as the central panel below. The decoration is completed by a cornice in stucco with lotus buds and clover. The decoration on the south wall is symmetrical, except for the main painting in the central part (see inventory 41657/cat. no. 7) and uses the standard iconography of Mars and Venus to show Alexander the Great and his wife Roxana (see Lagi De Caro 1988, pp. 75-88) or Statira, according to the most recent interpretation (see *Alessandro Magno*, 1995, p. 78).

The use of medallions with busts of single characters is common in fourth style paintings (see Miniero 1989, pp. 44-45; *Pompei. Pitture*, 1994, V, p. 878) or couples (see *Pompei. Pitture*, 1990, II, pp. 479, 648) which are sometimes idealised as in the famous portrait usually referred to as "Sappho" (see *Bellezza*, 1992, p. 104, no. 3) or given recognisable facial features, as in the very famous portrait of Terentius Neo, usually referred to as Paquius Proculus, and his wife (see *Le Collezioni*, 1989, I.1, p. 157, no. 236).

Paintings of Dionysian characters in circular or square medallions are very common in Pompeian painting (see inventory 20614, 17713/cat. nos. 22 and 23).   (C.C)

Bibl.: *Bellezza*, 1992, pp. 106-107, no. 6, with previous bibliography; Cicirelli, in *Pompeii. Picta fragmenta*, 1997, p. 96, no. 40; Cicirelli, in *Pitture nella Reggia*, 1999, p. 93, no. 54.

20. Medallion with female bust
Inv. no. 20610
Pompeii, V 3, 11
46 x 46 cm

A panel removed from a white wall features a medallion with a border surrounded by a cornice with double dentellation in a dark colour, with a half bust of a young woman with a fixed, absent gaze painted on a grey ground. Her face has noble features and a rosy complexion, and she is glancing to the right, her eyes looking up slightly and her lips just parted in a languid pose. A wreath of vegetation tied with a gold ribbon holds back her brown hair, which is parted down the middle and falls softly on her shoulders with kiss curls framing her face.

This figure wears a thin transparent dress, embellished with a conspicuous piece of jewellery round her neck, which is part of a torc necklace with a large green stone in the centre.

The medallion was detached from the west wall of the *triclinium* (I) which looks out on to the *viridarium* (G) of House V 3, 11, where in the final years of Pompeii a biclinium had been built outside – a view which could be enjoyed from Room I, lying on the same axis as the garden.

The *triclinium* is decorated with a painting in the fourth style and a socle imitating marble with rhomboid elements, a central tripartite section with two lateral yellow panels and a central

66   white one with ornate borders with a central medallion and small lateral squares, and a yellow frieze with garlands and a meander.

This medallion was originally part of the central panel of the west wall and formed a series with two other medallions showing busts of Ariadne and a Maenad, the former at the centre of the north wall, and the latter on the east wall, which clearly allude to the Dionysian cult and the tricliniar function of the room. The decorative theme shows the same stylistic features to be found in a group of paintings (see the decoration of the *caupona* of Euxinus) attributed to the atelier of Via di Castricio (see De Vos 1982, pp. 119-130) which flourished in Pompeii after the AD 62 earthquake. This atelier was also responsible for the paintings in the rooms where the medallion once stood. In fourth style paintings the use of medallions with busts of single characters is common, such as that of a young woman from Castellammare (see Miniero 1989, pp. 44-45) or of couples, like the female and adolescent busts at the House of the First Storey I 11, 15 (see *Pompei. Pitture*, 1990, II, p. 648). The female and male busts at the House of the Lovers (I 10, 10 - see *Pompei. Pitture*, 1990, II, p. 479) were sometimes idealised as in the famous portrait usually called Sappho (see *Bellezza*, 1992, p. 104, no. 3), and portrayed with recognisable facial features as in the very famous portrait of Terentius Neo (usually referred to as Paquius Proculus) and his wife (see *Le Collezioni*, 1989, I.1, p. 157, no. 236). In the vast picture gallery of Vesuvian paintings Dionysian characters in circular or square medallions are very common, both as single subjects and couples, for example, Maenad and Bacchus, Maenad and a Satyr, Maenad and Silenus in the act of embracing or offering each other a *kantharos* (see inventory 20614, 17713/cat. nos. 22 and 23; *Le Collezioni*, 1989, I.1, p. 160, no. 264; *Riscoprire Pompei*, 1994, pp. 289-290, no. 221).   (C.C)

Bibl.: *Pompei. Pitture*, 1991, pp. 944, 954; *Neapolis*, 1994, II, pp. 136-137; Cicirelli, in *Pompeii. Picta fragmenta*, 1997, p. 97, no. 41; Cicirelli, in *Pitture nella Reggia*, 1999, p. 94, no. 55.

21. Medallion with female bust

Inv. no. 20611
Pompeii VI 7, 20 and 22
(House of the Silverware)
46 x 46 cm

On the white wall is a medallion with a green wreath-like border. The medallion has a brown background and shows traces of a female bust, wearing a robe and holding a fan. She wears a diadem on her head and her thick shoulder-length hair is parted down the middle. She has long gold and pearl earrings, which are particularly well painted. Fine brushstrokes suggest the eyelids, nose and mouth, and realistic highlights and shading give volume to the face.

This medallion and another painting showing the bust of a boy were removed from the central part of the north wall in the exedra (Room 20) of the House of the Silverware. This room was decorated in the 4th style, and some fragments of the red socle and the central white section remain. The house was excavated between 1830 and 1840 and stands on Via di Mercurio in a largely residential area of Pompeii, with imposing mansions containing many wall paintings.

The custom of placing medallions with male and female busts on the central part of the walls, usually idealised and often with characters holding objects, was fairly common in 4th style Vesuvian paintings (Ling 1991, pp. 157-159). The most famous example, for the state of conservation and the realistic expression of the face, is the so-called "Sappho" discovered in a Pompeian residence in

1760 (*Le Collezioni*, 1989, I.1, p. 156, no. 232) with a medallion of a male bust.

Among the numerous medallions still at Pompeii and similar to this one in style are two paintings in Room R at the House of the Golden Cupids (*Pompei. Pitture*, 1994, V, p. 841, nos. 230 and 232) and two more in the vestibule at

House I 11, 6-7 (*Pompei. Pitture*, 1990, II, pp. 527-530). (E.D.C.)

Bibl.: *Pitture e Pavimenti*, 1983, II, p. 157; *Pompeii. Pitture*, 1993, IV, p. 446; De Carolis, in *Pompeii. Picta fragmenta*, 1997, p. 98, no. 42; De Carolis, in *Pitture nella Reggia*, 1999, p. 95, no. 56.

22. Small painting of busts of a Maenad and Silenus

Inv. no. 20614
Pompeii, unknown provenance
30 x 29 cm

A black *pinax* with a yellow and white border contains a picture of half busts of a Maenad and Silenus.

The Maenad in the foreground is turning slightly to the left; she wears a wreath of ivy, her straight brown hair has a parting down the middle and tied loosely at the neck, cascading on to her shoulders; she has a sensuous mouth highlighted with fine white brushstrokes and large expressive eyes, and wears two gold globe-shaped earrings. She is dressed in a violet tunic with a low neck, pinned to one shoulder, and loosely draped in a V shape at the front, showing off her pale skin.

Behind her right shoulder is the upper part of a green *thyrsus*. To the left, just behind the Maenad, is the naked bust of a tanned elderly Silenus, turning towards the young woman with a sensuous, mischievous gaze, his hand clasping her left shoulder.

Silenus wears an ivy wreath on his balding head, which is symbolised by the few sparse hairs remaining.

His expression is typically licentious, and his face is framed by a thick white beard with a drooping moustache, almost hiding his sensuous parted lips. This picture, of unknown provenance, was certainly part of a 4th style decoration, the presence of rectangular panels and medallions with busts of Dionysian and other characters being a typical feature in the central part of the wall. This style always presented these features with winged figures and birds on plain backgrounds, which alternated with *trompe l'oeil* vistas and were located above the central panel – the main feature of the whole wall decoration.

The use of small square paintings with bacchantes with a predominantly decorative function is often found in the wall paintings of the Vesuvian towns, where the cult of Dionysus and drinking was widespread.

The themes most frequently used were the couples Maenad-Satyr, Maenad-Silenus, Bacchus-Maenad, showing them embracing or more often holding or drinking from a *kantharos* (see Inv. 17713/cat. no. 23; *Le Collezioni*, 1989, I.1, p. 160, no. 264; *Riscoprire Pompei*, 1994, pp. 288, 290, no. 223).   (C.C.)

Bibl.: *Bellezza*, 1992, pp. 156-157, no. 10, with previous bibliography; Cicirelli, in *Pompeii. Picta fragmenta*, 1997, p. 100, no. 44; Cicirelli, in *Pitture nella Reggia*, 1999, p. 96, no. 57.

23. Square panel with busts of Maenad and Silenus

Inv. no. 17713
Pompeii VI 2, 22 (House of the Dancers)
46 x 45 cm

70

This is green panel is made up of small square paintings with red borders picked out in yellow.

In the centre of one of the paintings are the half busts of two bacchantes, tenderly embracing – a Maenad and an elderly Silenus.

The Maenad turns slightly to her right, and wears a wreath of vine leaves and berries, with brown shoulder-length hair and a sensuous face with a dreamy expression. She wears a light white mantle which has slipped off her shoulders. This part of the garment is suggested by the fine brushstrokes on her raised forearm, as if to emphasise the young girl's delicate flesh tones. These are highlighted by the strong light from the right, in clear contrast to the brown skin of the elderly Silenus whom the girl is tenderly embracing with her right arm round his neck, while with her left arm she holds out to him a silver *kantharos*. Old Silenus is balding and wears a beard and an ivy wreath on his head, which is easily identified by the features, sensuously nestling against the right cheek of the young Maenad. This painting comes from the House of the Dancers, whose decoration (now almost completely missing) is attributed to the 4th style and is of rather modest quality (see *Pompei. Pitture*, 1994, V, pp. 230-262).

Due to the improvised style of the painting, there are serious errors in the proportions, for example, in the hands of the Maenad.

The presence of small square panels and medallions with busts of bacchantes is frequent in wall paintings in the Vesuvian towns and has a decorative function. The allusion to the god of intoxication, to *joie de vivre*, fertility of the soil and happiness of life after death, was all important to the inhabitants of Pompeii, particularly to the followers of Dionysus, who was the protector of the main crop (the vine) which provided them with most of their wealth.

The most common themes are Bacchus and the Maenad, or couples such as Bacchus-Maenad or Maenad-Satyr, showing them embracing, or holding or drinking from a *kantharos* (see inv. 20614/cat. no. 22; *Le Collezioni*, 1989, I.1, p. 160, no. 264; *Riscoprire Pompei*, 1994, pp. 288, 290, no. 223).   (C.C.)

Bibl.: Cicirelli, in *Pompeii. Picta fragmenta*, 1997, p. 101, no. 45; Cicirelli, in *Pitture nella Reggia*, 1999, p. 97, no. 58.

24. Cupids and Psyche making sacrifices

Inv. no. 20879
Pompeii VII 4, 59 (House of the Bronzes)
60 x 53 cm

A panel removed from a black wall contains a *pinax* depicting a genre scene with cupids making sacrifices surrounded by a dark red border with white fillet on a pale background in an impressionistic style, the painting in shades of green and brown.

This pyramid-shaped composition contains elements which are typical of an idyllic sacred scene: an altar with trophies, a pedestal on which stands a statue of Juno portrayed as a slender winged figure wearing a long chiton turning to her left, and a leafy sacred tree which completes the picture in the background, painted with thick rapid brushstrokes.

These elements are the focal point of the composition, at the centre of the scene. On the right is a *Psyche* dressed in a long chiton with her head turned to her left shown offering a sacrifice to the goddess at the altar. Two chubby cupids with downy wings are shown on the left, one in the foreground chasing a peacock (the bird sacred to Juno), trying to catch it with both hands. The peacock in the centre is beautifully painted, and turns towards the would-be captor, while another cupid peeps cheerfully from behind the altar. The scene is completed in the foreground by an open box with the lid resting on it.

The style of painting is impressionistic, with the figures rendered in patches of light and shade, with strong brushstrokes in light and dark colours. It comes from the *triclinium* (Room y) at the House of the Black Wall, also called House of the Bronzes, excavated in first half of the 19th century. The decoration of the south wall, consisting of a bipartite composition, can be ascribed to the 4th style.

The socle comprises two panels with a medallion showing the head of a Gorgon separated by a narrow section with a gryphon. The central part contains two panels divided by an architectural view with a floral candelabrum above which are a globe and an eagle. These panels contain two pictures of cupids offering sacrifices, one to Juno on the left (the picture discussed here) and the other to Mars on the right (see Reinach 1922, p. 94, 2).

Above the cornice with corbels supported by giant figures terminating in serpents or sphinxes in small squares with sea monsters is a higher register which contains a central niche with Jupiter seated on a throne, next to a niche with a female figure making a sacrifice under a lamp held by a cupid. The two paintings on the south wall are part of the same series as the ones with the

same subject in the central part of the west wall – one showing cupids making sacrifices to Aphrodite before a statue of Priapus who holds a sceptre and a *rhyton* (see Reinach 1922, p. 89, 2), the other a scene with cupids making sacrifices to Dionysus (see Reinach 1922, p. 89, 3). The scenes on the wall and ceiling panels in the 4th style show flying cupids and *Psyche* with different attributes (see Reinach 1922, pp. 70-75) or genre compositions with characters engaged in various occupations associated with daily life or work. The best example of themes associated with games and amusement is the frieze in the *triclinium* of the House of the Vettii (see Reinach 1922, pp. 85-92). These subjects were popular in Pompeian painting, as were depictions of Eros in scenes inspired by the myth of Venus (see Reinach 1922, pp. 59-66).

For a study on representations of Eros, the most common subject in classical times, see Blanc, Gury and Leredde 1987, pp. 297-334.						(C.C.)

Bibl.: *Orangerie italiana*, 1991, p. 14; Cicirelli, in *Pompeii. Picta fragmenta*, 1997, pp. 110-111, no. 61; Cicirelli, in *Pitture nella Reggia*, 1999, p. 61, no. 30.

25. Landscape with mythological scene

Inv. no. 20880
Pompeii I 8, 5
(House of the Indian Statue)
50 x 42 cm

This small painting has a dark red border with a white fillet and was removed from a black wall. It is painted in shades of green and brown and shows a mythological scene in a setting reminiscent of an idyllic sacred landscape, where the characters are minute, like silhouettes, overwhelmed by the scale. They are painted with rapid brushstrokes in brown, except for two figures in the foreground on the right lying under a tree, who wear robes painted white in fine brushstrokes. This scene is difficult to interpret. It is set outside the town, and there are crenellated towers on the city gate shown on the left. In front of the arch are lightly drawn figures standing, two of whom appear to be conversing, almost as if one is delivering a message to the other, while three more characters are rushing towards a large rocky outcrop containing steps. This is vividly highlighted with thick white paint and behind it stands a leafy tree executed in rapid brushstrokes. Another tree can be seen in the foreground in whose shade two cloaked figures are lying, who cannot be identified.

In the background is a long colonnade with a tower surrounding a canal harbour, and a boat sails on the clear waters. This is a complex landscape and the setting for a mythological scene painted in a very original manner. The painting comes from the *tablinum* (Room 4) of the House of the Indian Statue, and was part of the third style decoration of the wall. It is a tripartite composition: the black socle is decorated with vegetation, the central part consists of three panels, the main one in black, containing the painting discussed here. The two lateral ones with red grounds

show pictures of animals, while in the upper part is a painted pilaster strip above the moulded cornice in stucco. Stylistically, the painting recalls the mythological scenes set in idyllic sacred landscapes, often complete with architectural vistas, which were a common feature of paintings in the centre of walls in the third and fourth style (see Peters 1963).

The small scale of the figures compared to the landscape elements is a novel feature. It suggests Roman eclecticism, and recalls the interesting rocky landscapes in episodes of the Odyssey, in particular the arrival of Ulysses in the country of the Laestrygonians, which can be seen on the walls of a house on the Esquiline (see Gallina 1964). In that painting the characters are also sketchy, though realistic, similar to the impressionistic technique used in the painting discussed here.   (C.C.)

Bibl.: *Neapolis*, 1994, II, pp. 133-134; Cicirelli, in *Pompeii. Picta fragmenta*, 1997, pp. 128-129, no. 81.

26. Hippolytus and Phaedra

Inv. no. 20620
Pompeii, unknown provenance
54 x 61 cm

The red wall, where this *pinax* originally stood, contained a painting surrounded by a thin white frame. The scene shows four figures: a seated woman on the left; three standing figures in the centre, and a horse and a dog on the right. In the middle is a male figure, standing upright facing the front. He is naked, with just a chlamys draped down his back on one side, and he holds a lance. The pose of the figure suggests he is resting, with the weight on his left leg

and his right leg slightly bent with the toes just touching the ground, raised as though about to take a step.

The movement towards the right, which the man is about to make, is developed in the upper part of the body, with a slight torsion of the bust, the movement stressed by the muscles in his chest, face and elbow. These are highlighted and stand out from the tanned skin, and with the bent right arm all suggest movement. However, the gesture of the

hand drawn back and the angry suspicious glance capture the attention and focus the gaze on the left side, where a female figure sits on an elegant throne.

She is sitting straight, facing the front. On her right arm is a fine armilla on an arm-rest in the form of a winged sphinx; her left arm is raised and a slender hand reaches up to her throat. She is turning slightly towards the centre of the scene and looking not at the protagonist but at the onlooker, her gaze frozen in the act of a tragic revelation. Over the yellow chiton she wears a purple mantle bordered in green, which clings to her body and shows her legs – the left one bent and the right one drawn back. These features suggest different reactions by the two characters in the foreground, and point to their identities and the event. The young man who is ready to go hunting is frozen in his tracks by the revelation, though he shows little sign of reacting to the news he has received, with just an exchange of glances and imperceptible movements.

In contrast, the woman who is more dramatically painted, appears regal and perturbed. The effect of the double register of the hands, the right hand resting loosely and the left raised to her throat in apprehension, the appearance of the figure in the picture planes and in perspective, the swirling folds of her dress – all this is contrasts with the powerful physique of the young man. Behind the main figures are two minor ones: an elderly woman in a long draped chiton and red head-dress, and a squire holding the reigns of an impatient white horse, moving to the right, followed by a hound.

In the background are two columns with a flag draped in between, and at the back is a second building silhouetted against a pale green sky. The architecture, like a stage set, predominates while the lack of nature is conveyed by the unnatural looking sky, which appears more the colour of a stormy sea. Light and shade is produced by a single source of light from the left. This composition recalls the stage sets and subjects of Greek tragedies which inspired Italian potters and artists during the 4th century BC. In the early 1st century AD a Campanian artist, known as the Hellenic Master as he worked in the Greek style consisting of placing the figures on intersecting planes, worked in Pompeii and Herculaneum. His paintings show the influence of early experiments by the Greeks of the depiction of a group in the picture space. Therefore, this work appears to be an imitation of Greek painting. The subject is inspired by the theatre and is the scene of Phaedra's confession to the young Hippolytus, about to go hunting. Infatuated with her stepson and rejected by him, Phaedra, the second wife of Theseus, commits suicide, falsely accusing Hippolytus of seduction. Similarities exist with a fresco from Herculaneum (*Le Collezioni*, 1989, I.1, p. 150, no. 195) and another painting from Stabiae (Miniero 1989, p. 36) showing Hipploytus repudiating Phaedra, part of a figurative composition now lost, with his step-mother and the old nurse. The myth of Hippolytus is frequent in wall painting and usually depicts the salient moments of the story, either in scenes with few figures (see *Le Collezioni*, 1989, I.1, no. 76) or in scenes like this one, which are more complex and detailed. The source for the iconography of the various scenes is the second "Hippolytus" by Euripides, which resulted in two versions of the story in the figurative arts: one in the Greek style focussing on the drama of Phaedra's love, the other covering the whole story in a theatrical representation showing the main characters. In this picture, the composition on different planes, the frontal poses and the figures slightly turning on the same plane are clearly of classical inspiration. However, the moods of the characters and the attempt to control the space (Phaedra's leg drawn back and the glimpse of Hippolytus's inclined right foot) suggest that the painting is in the tradition of the 3rd style.   (M.M.)

Bibl.: Mastroroberto, in *Riscoprire Pompei*, 1993, pp. 292-294, no. 225; Mastroroberto, in *Pompeii. Picta fragmenta*, 1997, pp. 116-117, no. 68; Mastroroberto, in *Pitture nella Reggia*, 1999, p. 62, no. 31.

Villa San Marco

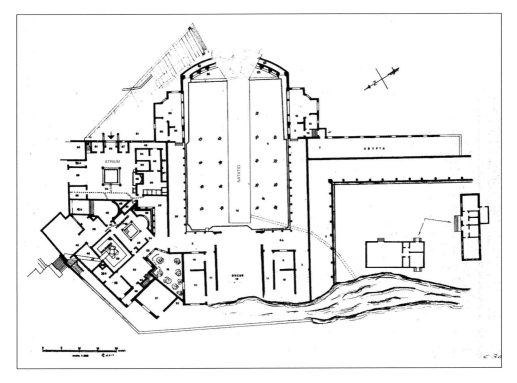

This villa is named after an 18th century chapel which stood nearby. The villa was situated at the north-eastern tip of the plain of Varano, a low-lying plateau in the area known today as Castellammare di Stabia, covering an area of about 11,000 sq. m. It was one of the largest Roman residences on the beautiful Campanian coast, which was developed from Cape Misenum to Punta della Campanella during the 1st century AD.

Buried by the eruption of Vesuvius in 79 AD, the villa was discovered and excavated in the Bourbon period between 1749 and 1754. A plan was made of it at the time and ornaments and decorations found there were put into the Royal Bourbon Museum in Portici, and are now part of the collections of the National Archeological Museum in Naples.

Finally revealed in its entirety between 1950 and 1962, the villa covers an area of around 6,000 sq. m, and consists of two large peristyles on different levels, with rooms distributed around them.

The oldest part of the building dates back to the Augustan period, and consists of rooms facing north-east. With the organisation peristyle-*tablinum-atrium*, following the precepts of Vitruvius, the main entrance (an open courtyard) was a road linking the villa to a small town, also excavated in Bourbon times and covering an area of around 45,000 sq. m, now destroyed.

The *atrium* with *compluvium*, which is the present-day entrance to the villa, has Ionic columns and is decorated with frescoes in the early 4th style. This is followed by the *tablinum*, four small rooms and a staircase leading to the first floor. The south-east wall has a *lararium* in a niche decorated in imitation marble, which was a typical feature in the Flavian period. On one side the atrium leads to the kitchen and service area and from the other

78

to a wide corridor with windows leading to the peristyle and baths. This is a large area and lies on a diagonal axis compared to the rest of the villa, consisting of a *frigidarium* with a large pool, a *tepidarium* and a *calidarium*, which was heated by a boiler immersed in the pool, still visible today.

The most spectacular part of the villa, extended and renovated in the Flavian period, is the large colonnade and garden with a *natatio*, thirty metres long, shaded by four rows of plane trees, terminating at the north end in a large *oecus* and decorated with giant paintings with flooring in *opus sectile* tiles. This area had a wonderful view over the Bay, and to the south was a magnificent semi-circular *nymphaeum*, decorated with stucco and pictures in glass mosaic, creating an impressive picture silhouetted against the green Lattari mountains.

Facing on to the colonnade are beautifully frescoed reception rooms in the 4th Flavian style, with iconographical themes and stylistic features of superb quality, which suggest a commission from the court environment.

The extension of the original dwelling to include an adjoining villa to the west on a higher level was carried out towards the end of the villa's existence, just before the eruption. The buildings were joined by a long ramp which rose five metres to compensate for the difference in height, leading to a splendid *porticus triplex* with a gallery of twisted columns in white plaster with a complex ceiling painting. This was being completed in 79 AD, and consisted of figurative compositions showing gods and mythological characters on large elaborate ceilings, which probably followed the *ambulatio* of the colonnade.

The structure of the villa follows the landscape of the site using ambitious engineering solutions: thus in the design of the building nature and architecture create a harmonious unity in which all the elements complement one another.

Unfortunately it has not been possible to discover who the owners of this fine suburban villa were, though the information available suggests that they may have been an old patrician family linked to the Imperial court, rather than *nouveaux riches*.   (A.M.S.)

Bibliography

Barbet A. - Miniero P. (ed. by), *La Villa S. Marco a Stabia*, Naples-Rome-Pompeii, 1999; Barbet A., *La Villa S. Marco*, in *In stabiano. Cultura e archeologia da Stabiae: la città e il territorio tra l'età arcaica e l'età romana*, exhibition catalogue, Castellammare di Stabia 2001, pp. 25-28.

27. Melpomene

Inv. no. 62523
Castellammare di Stabia, Varano,
Villa San Marco
143 x 111 cm

This fresco, a great deal of which is missing, represents Melpomene, the Muse of Tragedy, within a square panel with a white background surrounded by a blue border with wave motifs. Below is a dark red band with volutes and facing gryphons painted gold.

Melpomene is standing, turning slightly to the right, with her lips parted, looking up. On her head she wears sprigs of laurel and a yellow mantle covers her head, revealing dark curls which frame her face. She is dressed in a long, wide, green chiton and a yellow mantle falls in folds down her left side. The Muse holds a mask of an old bearded man in her left hand and a *pedum* is held diagonally in her right. This panel was the decoration on the south side of the fourth section of the ceiling in gallery 1 of the villa. Here the decoration consisted of large compositions with a central figurative painting. The central part of this section showed the figure of Mercury.

There are many depictions of the muse Melpomene, who is always shown with one of her two attributes (see Helbig 1868, p. 175, nos. 871-877, sv. *Melpomene*; Schefold 1957, p. 371, sv. *Muse*).

This painting is one of the most expressive versions of the Muse and can be dated to the Neronian-Flavian period (around 62-79 AD).   (G.B.)

Bibl.: Elia 1957, p. 36, Pl. IX; Miniero 1989, pp. 74-76; Bonifacio, in *Pitture nella Reggia*, 1999, p. 37, no. 7; Pedroso, in *La villa S. Marco a Stabia*, 1999, p. 274, no. 4.3.

28. Minerva

Inv. no. 62524
Castellammare di Stabia, Varano,
Villa San Marco
100 x 114 cm

80   Only a few fragments remain of this
panel, which was once the principal
decoration in the second section of the
ceiling of gallery 1 of the villa, following
the section with an armillary sphere
(inv. nos. 62464, 62525, 63718).
In the centre is a winged female figure
with a laurel wreath round her head,
holding a round shield with her left
hand and a long pole held diagonally;
with her right hand she clasps a long
branch with large thorns.
Behind her stands Minerva, her left arm
folded across her breast, and her right
hand in the act of putting a plumed
helmet on her head.
Her hair is auburn and partly revealed
under the golden helmet; she is looking
down to the left, her expression pensive
and a little sad.
On the left are traces of another figure.
The scene was part of a much larger
painting, which has been lost, probably
depicting the apotheosis of Minerva
carried by a Winged Victory. The couple
is silhouetted against a neutral
background.
The animation suggested by the open
wings, the movement of the panels and
the gesture of Minerva putting on a
helmet, contrast with the 0rigidity of the
Winged Victory and the heavy shield she
holds.
The iconography of the goddess Minerva
in this painting is unlike the traditional
version of *Athena Promachos*, which is

frequently found in Pompeii.
This type of representation is typical of
scenes of apotheosis found frequently on
monuments relating to Imperial Roman
art (see Helbig 1868, no. 153 *et seqq.*).
(G.B.)

Bibl.: Elia 1957, pp. 30-32, Pl. III;
Bonifacio, in *Pitture nella Reggia*,
1999, p. 33, no. 3; Pedroso, in *La villa
S. Marco a Stabia*, 1999, p. 272, no. 2.1.

Villa Arianna

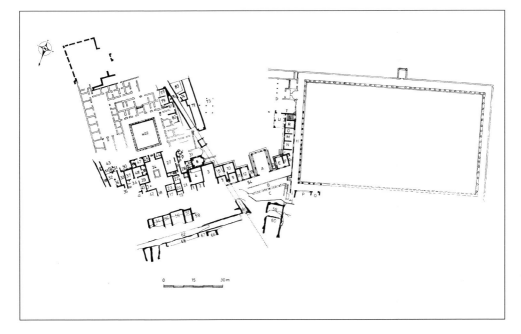

Built in a splendid position overlooking the plain of Varano, this villa is one of several large residential complexes which have not yet been fully completely excavated.

The villa was discovered and partially excavated during the Bourbon period in two stages (1757-1762 and 1777-1778), firstly under the direction of C. Weber, subsequently of F. La Vega. The main purpose of the excavations was to find objects, paintings and mosaics for the royal palace of Portici, later moved to the Royal Palace in Naples and finally the National Archeological Museum in the city.

During those excavations plans were made of the buildings discovered which were later collected together and published by M. Ruggiero in 1881 (1).

Further explorations of the villa were carried out starting on 16th February 1950, which brought much more of the structure to light, giving a clear idea of the form. The success of this work was partly due to L. D'Orsi, who revealed the rooms situated on the brow of the hill covering about 3,000 square metres.

Many frescoes discovered had been left *in situ* in the Bour-

bon period, but later removed or taken away to be conserved at the Stabian Antiquarium, which was in the process of being built.

This villa is named after the fresco which decorates the far wall of the *triclinium* (3). The building is complex in layout partly because of various alterations carried out over the years but also because the villa followed the morphology of the hillside.

The original nucleus of the villa dates back to the 1st century BC, and consists of a peristyle (W22) which is still completely buried, a Tuscan-style *atrium* (24) and a *tablinum* (18) following the principles of Vitruvius, organising suburban houses according to a scheme of peristyle-*atrium-tablinum*.

East of the *tablinum* is Room 42 which has a beautiful view and a fine wall painting in the 3rd style with a yellow socle. The corridor (40) leads to a courtyard (34) onto which several rooms open used for storage, and a staircase leads to the upper floor with stairs covered in tiles and two arches.

Proceeding eastwards the boundary between Villa Arianna and the adjoining one can be seen. This is referred to as "Secondo complesso" (the second complex) and consists of a narrow *vicus* (18) showing the height of this group of luxurious buildings situated on the plain of Varano in the 1st century AD.

Turning back, beyond the *tablinum* are more rooms with views (17-19) and a group of rooms for various purposes including baths situated round the courtyard (21). In the south corner of the courtyard is a pool surrounded by columns.

Continuing westwards, next is a large *triclinium* (3) which overlooks the Bay, with walls painted in the 4th style from the Neronian period.

At the centre of each wall are large mythological paintings with architectural features at the sides framed by columns, with a high red socle, decorated with single figures in niches against a black background.

On the far wall of this room a fresco showing Dionysus and Ariadne was discovered on 14th April 1950. On the east wall a fresco was found depicting the myth of Hippolytus and Phaedra, while on the west wall a fresco appears with the myth of the nymph Ambrosia killed by Lycurgus, which at the time of the excavation had almost fallen through to the outside.

Another part of the villa consists of four rooms (5-7-9-10) served by a corridor (8) which can be considered the living area. This was used by the owners of the villa during the summer as it looked towards the sea, with inner rooms whose windows faced the Lattari mountains.

Following this group is another suite of rooms with views (11-L) added to the villa during the Flavian period, during an extension made to connect it with another building which includes the rooms from north to west and the large peristyle (H) which was incorporated into the Villa Arianna.

This peristyle has only been partly uncovered in excavations between 19th December 1777 and 30th April 1778. It had a perimeter of 104 x 81 metres, twice the length of a Roman stadium, and the same length that Vitruvius recommended for the colonnades of *palaestrae*.

It was reached from the south by a small gallery (60) with a clay floor and steps in Vesuvian lava stone.

The villa was connected to the valley below by a series of ramps on six levels, which provided access under the living quarters to the rural area. Here, in 1981, a courtyard was discovered with the remains of two farm carts.   (G.B.)

Bibliography

Ruggiero M., *Degli scavi di Stabiae dal 1749 al 1782*, Naples 1881; Elia O., *Pitture di Stabia*, Naples 1957, pp. 57-74; D'Orsi L., *Gli scavi archeologici di Stabiae*, Milan 1968; Robotti C., *Una sinopia musiva pavimentale a Stabia* in "BdA", ser. 5, vol. 58, 1973, pp. 42-44; Allroggen Bedel A., *Die Wandmalerein aus der Villa in Campo Varano (Castellammare di Stabia)* in "Römische Mitteilungen", 84, 1977, pp. 27-89; Barbet A., *La peinture murale romaine*, Paris 1985, pp. 249-254; Camardo D. - Ferrara A. - Longobardi N., *Stabiae: le ville, Castellammare di Stabia*, 1989, pp. 17-40; Miniero P., *Stabiae. Pitture e stucchi delle ville romane*, exhibition catalogue, Naples, 1989, pp. 19-24; Pisapia M.S., *Mosaici antichi in Italia. Regione I, Stabiae*, Rome 1989, pp. 35-50; D'Orsi L., *Gli scavi di Stabiae. Giornale di scavo a cura di A. Carosella*, Rome 1996 *passim*; Bonifacio G., in *In Stabiano. Cultura e archeologia da Stabiae: la città e il territorio tra l'età arcaica e l'età romana*, Castellammare di Stabia 2001, pp. 29-30.

29. Hippolytus

Inv. no. 62527
Stabiae, Villa Arianna, *triclinium*
70 x 140 cm

The reconstructed fragments depict Hippolytus, a famous character in the world of Greek tragedy. This myth, which was handed down via the second Euripidean version of the drama *Hippolytus with the Crown* was revisited in Roman times, the most famous version being Seneca's *Phaedra*.

The male figure in the painting, once thought to be Theseus (Elia 1957, p. 65) is more likely to be his famous son Hippolytus, the protagonist of the legend in which he is the object of the unrequited love of Phaedra, second wife of his father. In Euripedes' drama Hippolytus is described as a devotee of Artemis, the solitary verginal goddess, while his mother-in-law venerates Aphrodite; both characters are driven by emotion, and represent the conflict between spirit and matter.

Hippolytus scorns Phaedra's love, and drives the drama to a tragic conclusion resulting in the death of the protagonists and the triumph of Theseus's wisdom, a quality which makes the ideal sovereign – just but firm. The drama depicted in this painting from Stabiae is the second part of the story, where Hippolytus restrained by the nurse gives vent to his horror and scorn of women. The drama of facing such a fearful situation becomes intensely theatrical with the gesture of the hand thrust forward, also found in several well-known variations from Pompeii and Herculaneum (see *Riscoprire Pompei*, 1993, pp. 292-294, Pl. 225).

In this fresco Hippolytus is shown preparing to go hunting, dressed in a purple chlamys as he looks to his right. His glance suggests the rest of the scene, now lost, with the exit from the palace on the right and Phaedra's nurse on the left. The anatomical details are particularly accurate in the bold rendering of the hand in perspective and the calculated

expression of amazement on his face, which is elongated with heavily marked features. His forehead is covered by long, wavy locks, his lips are full and his nose is prominent, in an image which has nothing in common with the idealised versions of previous works in the 3rd style. This realism is possibly because this was a portrait of an actor, explaining why he is not shown naked as the traditional hero would have been (for more information on actors of pantomimes, the real "heroes" of the people and the court, see Carcopino 1987, pp. 252-264). This large-scale

theatrical scene was probably a *megalografia* on the north-east wall of the splendid *triclinium* of the villa, which contained another of Euripides' dramas with Pilades among the protagonists (inv. no. 62528). It is typical of the 4th style from the Neronian period, showing a clear progression towards a more Roman style, less influenced by Greek art.   (M.M.)

Bibl.: Elia 1951, p. 45, Pl. 5-6; Elia 1957, p. 58; Miniero 1989, pp. 36-37; Mastroroberto, in *In Stabiano*, 2001, p. 131, no. 241.

Villa del Petraro

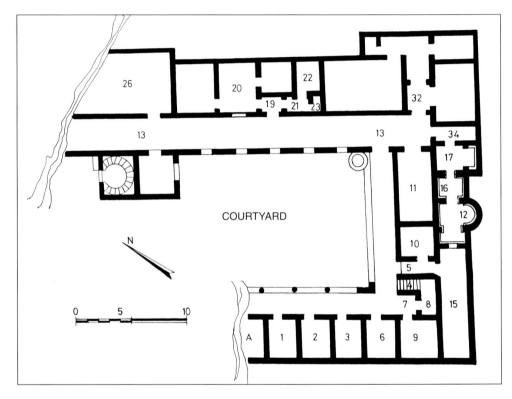

A Roman villa buried by the eruption of Vesuvius in 79 AD was discovered in 1957 in a hilly area near Santa Maria la Carità, originally part of the *ager stabianus* (the countryside near Stabiae).

The site of the villa, affected by a landslide, covered an area of around 1,000 sq. m, with a rectangular plan and west-facing entrance. It consisted of a central courtyard with living quarters and service rooms distributed round it, in the traditional manner.

The courtyard was bordered by a colonnade on the south and east sides and a long cryptoporticus with windows on the north side.

The south wing of the villa was occupied by a suite of six rooms, all similar, opening on to a narrow galleried corridor without any wall paintings, the layout suggesting a series of *ergastula* or storage areas.

Five rooms gave on to the north-facing cryptoporticus, comprising living rooms and *cubicula*, while facing the courtyard were two small rooms, probably service areas for unidentified functions.

The east side of the villa era was entirely taken up by the baths, consisting of a rectangular *apodyterium* and a *frigidarium*, a square *tepidarium* and *calidarium* with an apse.

In 79 AD large-scale renovation work was being done throughout the villa, as evidenced by the incomplete state of some of the structures and the piles of building materials found, particularly in the baths area. In the *frigidarium* preparations were being made to position the pool for cold-water bathing, which would occupy the entire east wall of the room. In the *tepidarium* work on the heating system was in progress, consisting of earthenware pipes, while in the *calidarium*, where the heating method used was *concamerationes*, the flooring was being laid. The room in the south-west corner, communicating with the *hypocaustum* and the *calidarium* through an opening in the north wall, was the *praefurnium* for the baths.

The *thermae* were part of the original plan of the villa, judging from the projections of the apse and of the *calidarium* in the perimeter wall, the use of *opera incerta* and the presence of earthenware pipes, a heating system which was older than the *suspensurae* built in brick columns.

The first construction phase of the villa dates back to the early Augustan period, judging from the use of Sarnian limestone in *opera incerta* in the perimeter wall and in some internal structures. The second phase, in progress in 79 AD, used the method of *opera vittata*.

At the same time as the structural renovation, decoration in stucco was being carried out in the baths area. These decorations in the Neronian style suggest that taste was a little out of date in the provinces, though they subscribed to the themes typical of Pompeian painting in the Flavian period.

The domestic objects found in the north wing were mostly utilitarian objects, with few elaborate pieces in bronze, glass or fine pottery. These finds contrast with the fine complex stucco decoration in the baths, suggesting a change in ownership and possibly in use of the building. However, the incomplete state of the work makes it difficult to understand what the purpose of the renovation was.   (A.M.S)

Bibliography

De Caro S., *Villa rustica in località Petraro*, in "RIASA", III, X, 1987, pp. 5-89; Sodo A.M., in *In Stabiano. Cultura e archeologia da Stabiae: la città e il territorio tra l'età arcaica e l'età romana*, exhibition catalogue, Castellammare di Stabia 2001, pp. 33-34.

30. Narcissus at the fountain

Inv. no. 61002
Santa Maria la Carità, Petraro, villa
95 x 95 cm

This painting represents the myth of the young Narcissus at the fountain, which decorated the west wall of the *frigidarium* at the villa, framed by ridged pilaster strips with cushion capitals and necking with *ovoli*. The white plaster base has a double cornice with *ovoli* and fillets, showing a young man in a dominant position, seated in a languid pose on a rock. His right hand clasps a fold of the mantle which covers his shoulders and his knee, while the left hand rests on the rock, acting as a support. His head is slightly bent, and his hair is long and wavy with strong chiaroscuro tones. His legs, like the rest of his body, hang loosely: the right leg is bent and the left extended in the foreground, resting on the base of the column which frames the scene on the left. The young man is looking towards a pool, which can be glimpsed below the rock and reflects his face. Behind him to the right a cupid advances holding a torch, the light shining down, who is the bearer of the sad omen of death.

The scene consists of the column in the foreground, a simple structural element, and on the opposite side a large leafy tree with highlights in chiaroscuro showing jagged branches laden with leaves.

This scene is typical of the many versions of the myth painted in the Vesuvian area. The allusion to water is perfect for an environment like the *frigidarium*, and recurs in the representation of the river god which decorated the facing wall in the same room.

The decorative style, classicism and impressionist technique are typical of the Neronian period. This painting shows stylistic features of an atelier working just before the eruption of Vesuvius. In fact, the decoration of the baths was halted by the catastrophe on 24th August 79 AD while it was still being painted, as is evident from the excavations. (A.M.S.)

Bibl.: De Caro 1987, pp. 17-19, fig. 12 and bibliography already mentioned; Sodo, in *In stabiano*, 2001, p. 138, no. 262.

31. Satyr riding a goat

Inv. no. 60971
Santa Maria la Carità, Petraro, villa
63.5 x 56 cm

This panel shows a young satyr riding a goat, moving towards the left, in a frame with a listel fillet and a fascia.

The satyr is virtually naked and only has a light mantle flapping round his shoulders. In his left hand is a plate of small fruit and with his right he is holding on to the goat's neck. He is pictured from the left, and has bushy hair.

On the left a fragment of another border was probably the frame of the adjoining panel; at the bottom is a double cornice with stylised floral motifs which is now part of the upper area of the wall where it joins the ceiling.

In the bottom left-hand corner, at the join between the two coffers is a high relief of a small satyr's head seen from the left. The panel was found in the vault of the apse. It belonged to the decoration of the ceiling of the *calidarium* (Room 12) and is similar to another satyr with a *rhyton* (inv. no. 60972) and a winged Psyche (inv. no. 60986). The discovery of these panels, some of which are part of a series, has made it possible to reconstruct the decorative scheme of the entire ceiling of the *calidarium*, consisting of a barrel vault divided into square coffers, each of which had a figure in the centre.   (G.B.)

Bibl.: Mielsch 1975, p. 130, Pl. 31-32; De Caro, 1987, p. 30, Pl. 36; Miniero 1989, p. 82, no. 23; Bonifacio, in *Pompeii. Picta Fragmenta*, 1997, pp. 72-73; Bonifacio, in *In Stabiano*, 2001, p. 140, no. 266.

32. Phoenix

Inv. no. 41671
Pompeii I 11, 10-11
(*Caupona* of Euxinus)
123 x 124 cm

This fresco on a white ground shows a bird, which can be identified as a pheasant by its yellow and red plumage, in profile among vegetation and flowers with other birds in flight or perched on branches. The upper part of the painting is decorated with a floral garland tied at the ends and in the middle forming festoons. The pheasant has an Egyptian crown on its head shaped like a sun between horns, and suggests the mythical phoenix, the symbol of the resurrection. Below are the words: PHOENIX.FELIX.ET.TV. At the bottom of the painting are two facing peacocks among vegetation.

This fresco was situated outside, on the left-hand column at the entrance to the *Caupona* of Euxinus, discovered in 1955 during the excavations directed by Amedeo Maiuri in Regions I and II. It has been possible to identify the owner thanks to the discovery inside the building of three amphorae bearing his name and an electoral manifesto in which Euxinus recommends the election of Q. Postumius and M. Cerrinius as *aediles* in the town. The tavern where Euxinus lodged is one of the many premises used for catering strategically placed near the Amphitheatre and the Great Palaestra, which were obviously very popular with the local inhabitants. The inscription painted below the image of the phoenix can be translated as "The phoenix is happy [I hope it is] and you

too", which can be interpreted as a wish that the customers of the tavern will continue to drink there. The fresco with the phoenix is part of a group of vernacular paintings (see *La pittura di Pompei*, 1991, pp. 267-273) which are helpful in identifying businesses, a type of painting not found in the other Vesuvian towns. (E.D.C.)

Bibl.: Pompei, 1973, no. 213; *Pompei 1748-1980*, 1981, pp. 159-160; *Pitture e Pavimenti*, 1981, I, p. 156; *Pompei. Pitture*, 1990, II, p. 572; De Carolis, in *Pompeii. Picta fragmenta*, 1997, p. 164, no. 147; De Carolis, in *Pitture nella Reggia*, 1999, p. 89, no. 50.

33. Nile scene

Inv. no. 41654
Pompeii VIII 7, 23-24
(House of the Sculptor)
78 x 209 cm

This rectangular frieze portrays a complex Nile scene. Starting from the left, there is a tower with two windows emerging from the water among shrubs and tree trunks with two ducks nearby swimming towards the right, quacking with open beaks. Next, shown among curving palms and shrubs, is a pirogue with a phallic shaped prow and at the stern is the helmsman's seat, high and curved, ending in a circular element. In the middle of the pirogue two naked pigmies are dancing, another pigmy is at the prow on the phallus, who seems to be clapping in time to the dance. Between the first dancing pigmy and the one at the prow the profile of another character's face can be glimpsed, possibly a dwarf juggler. The scene is completed by a bare tree and a woman making a sacrifice.

This fragment was part of a much larger composition, of which about 24 centimetres with many missing parts has been salvaged, depicting a Nile scene which decorated the socle of the north, south and east walls of the peristyle at the House of the Sculptor. This dwelling was discovered between 1796 and 1798,

and is named after the many complete or partially finished sculptures found inside (Mustilli 1950, pp. 215 *et seqq*.). This fresco is painted in the 2nd style and was covered by superstructures and alterations made to the house after the 62 AD earthquake. It dates back to the early Augustan age, according to Amedeo Maiuri (Maiuri 1955, p. 73). The whole composition would have shown themes and motifs relating to the Nile with caricatures of animals, pigmies and black people. This type of scene would also contain many erotic elements (Jacobelli 1995, p. 88), which were inspired by Alexandrine painting in the Hellenstic period (Ling 1991, pp. 165-167). These were very popular in Roman times due to the sensations they aroused, their grotesque and imaginary forms conjuring up an exotic world which fired the owner's imagination. While only this particular frieze has been found among the frescoes in Pompeii, there are many other examples of similar compositions on walls in private buildings and baths.
There were Nile scenes in the *frigidarium* of the Sarnian Baths

(*Terme del Sarno*, 1991, p. 12), in the *natatio* of the Suburban Baths (*Pompei*, 1992, II, p. 174) and, now missing, in the side rooms of the pool at the Stabian Baths (De Vos 1979, pp. 81-97). Other examples can be found in houses, for example in the *oecus* of House IX, 5, 9 (Whitehouse 1977, pp. 61-63) and in the atrium of the House of Menander (*Pompei. Pitture*, 1990, II, p. 245). A marine scene with an island in the background and pigmies on ships is, rather surprisingly, painted on the base of the Tomb of Vestorius Priscus at Pompeii (Spano 1943, pp. 285-288, fig. 11; Mols-Moorman 1993-1994, pp. 42-43). Finally, there are three frescoes, one showing a fight between pigmies and Nile animals, which are kept at the National Archeological Museum in Naples (*Pompei*, 1973, nos. 158-160).

(E.D.C.)

Bibl.: Maiuri 1955, pp. 65-80; *Pitture e Pavimenti*, 1983, III, pp. 369-370; De Carolis, in *Pompeii. Picta fragmenta*, 1997, p. 112, no. 63; De Carolis, in *Pitture nella Reggia*, 1999, p. 83, no. 45.

34. Aristaeus

Inv. no. 10437
Pompeii, I 11, 6 (House of the Venus
in Bikini)
77 x 34 cm

This statue represents a young upright figure, with the left leg bent resting on a small rock. The lower part of the body is covered by drapes of heavy cloth, suggested by the thickness around the raised leg, the drapery proceeding from the hips up the left arm, then falling to a double hem of small clinging folds with zig-zag edges. The left arm is missing below the folds of the mantle. Using realistic colours the whole of the lower body is divided into three parallel vertical sections, the two outer ones with chiaroscuro elements produced by the complex movement of the cloth, while the central one, corresponding to the left leg, is smooth and light in colour. The figure wears sandals. The draped garment has many folds, and a large pleat of the mantle at the left side conceals a support. In the draping round the hips the folds are carefully arranged. At the right hip, which projects, the torso is slightly curved to the left. The right arm is akimbo on his hip.

The modelling of the torso is agile and fluid, and the right shoulder soft and gentle, clearly showing Greek influence. The head is slightly turned towards his right shoulder, and his chest, like his back, is well-proportioned.

His face, almost oval in shape, has strong features: the eyebrows arch downwards over the temples which are framed by flowing regular locks of hair. The smooth skin of his face contrasts with his hair, which has traces of colour, and is held back by a band, his curls flowing down the nape of his neck. The particular plasticity of his face is from the post-Lisippean period, judging from the carving and modelling which features soft chiaroscuro effects, contrasting with the wavy hair.

This well-proportioned and attractive figure of a youth, beardless and naked, is possibly a divinity. The form, inclined to the left with a clear torsion of the bust, emphasises the rising line of the mantle to the left shoulder, and suggests Aristaeus. Son of the nymph Cyrene and Apollo, Aristaeus is credited with discovering how to milk cows, keep bees and grow vines. The god of the beneficial forces of Nature, his cult was particularly strong in Cyrene (see Paribeni 1959, nos. 197-222). As a chthonic divinity Aristaeus is often portrayed like Dionysus, who helped the god to conquer India, according to one story. The type, pose and semi-nakedness of the figure have some features in common with the type of Aphrodite Pontia. This work can be dated to around the first half of the 1st century AD and was discovered on the floor of the *tablinum* at the House called the Venus in Bikini. Also discovered here was the famous statue of Aphrodite, now at the National Archeological Museum in Naples (*Le Collezioni*, 1989, I.2, no. 254, p. 146). (M.M.)

Bibl.: Mastroroberto, in *Domus Viridaria Horti Picti*, 1992, pp. 106-107, no. 7.

35. Cloven-hoofed Pan
Inv. no. 3682
Pompeii, I 7, 11
(House of the Adolescent)
60 x 30 cm

This small statue is of a naked Pan with cloven hooves, carrying a *kalathos* full of fruit in his crooked left arm from which a fawn skin hangs. In his right hand is a goat's head – a sacrifice to Dionysus. The figure has a cunning expression, he is frowning and his prominent chin is covered by an untidy short beard. On his forehead are two small horns, just visible among his thick hair. Pan is usually represented as a demon, half man and half beast. In this picture his lower limbs are those of a goat with cloven hooves. The prodigious agility of this divinity, the protector of shepherds and their flocks, is also apparent in this small sculpture from Pompeii, which shows Pan upright. The animation of the composition is provided by the movement between the different inclination of the planes – Pan moving towards the right with one hoof ready to jump sideways, while his torso is twisted to the left, possibly attracted by the proximity of a nymph. Myths about Pan are rare and legends in the literary tradition about him are late, usually associated with the Alexandrines. Pan with cloven hooves is usually shown in Roman compositions of erotic Dionysian groups, of which there were numerous variations throughout the 2nd century BC, alone or in groups. There are various statues of Pan in gardens at Pompeii. This sculpture was discovered during excavations at the House of the Adolescent in 19 fragments with traces of gilding on the folds and lines of the muscles, indicating that the whole work was gilded. The same excavations brought to light a rectangular base with the remains of two cloven hooves, possibly from a statue of the same divinity (inv. no. 3685). Both statues were found in the *triclinium*. Judging from the treatment of the surfaces and the use of the drill this statue can be attributed to the Flavian period.   (M.M.)

Bibl.: Maiuri 1927, p. 72, Pl. 33; Mastroroberto, in *Domus Viridaria Horti Picti*, 1992, pp. 108-109, no. 10; Jashemski 1993, p. 40, Pl. 42.

The Villa of Poppaea at Oplontis

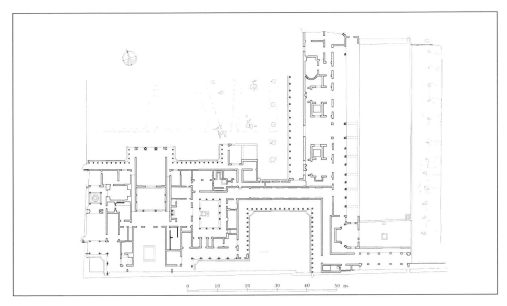

The so-called Villa of Poppaea was partially excavated between 1964 and 1984, which probably belonged for some time to the family of the Emperor Nero. The villa stands at the centre of the modern town of Torre Annunziata, known as Oplontis in antiquity, and a small urban centre in the suburbs of Pompeii. The oldest part of the villa dates back to the mid 1st century AD and consists of an atrium surrounded by a number of rooms. In 79 AD, the year in which Pompeii was destroyed by the eruption of Vesuvius, the villa was being rebuilt, possibly due to damage sustained during the AD 62 earthquake.

The entrance to the villa was from the south, beyond the present-day Canale Conte di Sarno. Along the single central axis were the atrium, now missing its columns, a large passage way, a *viridarium* and finally an *oecus*. This was probably a large dining room added in the Augustan period to the original building, open with two high columns facing towards the garden to the north. Along the sides are two colonnades, the east colonnade still completely buried beneath the modern road.

To the west of the central axis various types of rooms were (an *oecus* or reception room), a *triclinium* and a small bedroom which faced the sea. Also facing west were the baths with *tepidarium* and *calidarium*, and a small tetrastyle *atrium* with a circular fountain. The main feature of the oldest part of the building is the splendid painting in the 2nd Pompeian style, showing *trompe l'oeil* views of architecture.

The eastern part was built at the height of the Empire and consists of a large pool over 60 metres long. Along the western side of the pool ran a colonnade, from which the columns had been temporarily removed. Several fine rooms can be seen here, separated by a central reception room with high columns at the entrance to the pool, including some *viridaria* with wall paintings of gardens.

Among the objects of particular historical and artistic importance discovered at the villa during excavations were marble sculptures, most of which are good Roman copies of original Greek works from the Hellenistic period. These sculptures, which are of great decorative value, originally stood in the villa's gardens. The finds from the villa reveals interesting information about the taste of the Roman patricians, who were particularly fond of works of art placed in a natural setting. (L.F.)

36. Herm of Hercules

Inv. no. 3300
Torre Annunziata (Oplontis),
Villa of Poppaea
h 44 cm; side of base 27.1 cm

94

This head of a beardless young man in white marble, originally placed on a small column by the side of the pool, is probably Hercules. He has a sorrowful expression, emphasised by the deep-set eyes and slightly parted lips. He wears a wreath of flowers tied with a ribbon set on his unruly hair. The subject derives from a sculpture by the Greak Skopas 4th century BC, suggested by the modelling of the eyes, and more generally, by the intense expression.

(L.F.)

Bibl.: De Caro 1987, pp. 102-104;
Pompei. Abitare 1996, p. 268, no. 601.

37. Statue of a boy with a goose

Inv. no. 56 + 4987
Torre Annunziata (Oplontis),
Villa of Poppaea
h 46 cm; sides of base 67 x 35.5 cm

This small group in white marble was also part of a fountain decoration. It represents a naked boy whose right arm is clasping a goose and whose left hand is holding it by the neck. The figurative theme of the boy with the goose dates back to the early 2nd century BC, inspired by Boethos of Chalcedon. The many variations and copies show how popular this theme was in the Roman world. This copy dates back to the early 1st century AD. (L.F.)

Bibl.: De Caro 1987, pp. 94-96; *Pompei. Abitare* 1996, p. 267, no. 594.

38. Small statue of Aphrodite

Inv. no. 1252
Torre Annunziata (Oplontis),
Villa of Poppaea
h 52.5 cm; diam. at base 23.5 cm

96   The goddess is naked and shown in the
act of preparing for a bath. Her left foot
is resting on the wings of a cupid and
her left arm on a small female statue, a
priestess or a devotee, depicted standing
on a high pedestal. The original model
of this theme, which has been copied in
different ways, dates back to the late 3rd-
early 2nd century BC. The Oplontis copy,
in white marble with traces of colour, is
from the late 1st century BC.   (L.F.)

Bibl.: De Caro 1987, p. 114; *Pompei.
Abitare* 1996, p. 267, no. 593.

39. Statue of a female centaur

Inv. no. 71 + 1357
Torre Annunziata (Oplontis),
Villa of Poppaea
h 99 cm; sides of base 36.5 x 59.5 cm

This sculptural group, mentioned in the previous entry, comprised two male and two female centaurs. This female centaur is similar in form to the other centaurs, and wears a deer-skin; her hair is thick and wavy. On her right shoulder she carries a deer, and in her left a club. The group of four centaurs is a Roman copy from an original sculpture of the 2nd century AD, of Pergamum influence, and was originally placed in the garden north of the *atrium*.   (L.F.)

Bibl.: De Caro 1987, p. 88; *Pompei. Abitare* 1996, pp. 266-267, no. 588.

40. Group with satyr and hermaphrodite

Inv. no. 2800
Torre Annunziata (Oplontis),
Villa of Poppaea
h 100 cm; base 91 x 58 cm

This marble group, which was restored in antiquity, was discovered at one side of the pool and shows a hermaphrodite attacking a satyr. This example from Oplontis is one of many copies from a Greek original, whose iconography was presumably very popular as a decorative theme in the holiday villas belonging to Roman patricians.　　　　(L.F.)

Bibl.: De Caro 1987, pp. 98-100; *Pompei. Abitare* 1996, p. 268, no. 602.

41. Statue of a centaur

Inv. no. 70
Torre Annunziata (Oplontis),
Villa of Poppaea
h 90 cm

This sculpture, with four others, comprised a decorative group for a fountain in white marble, as evidenced by the hole in the centre. The centaur has a beard and is shown rearing up, wearing a ram skin, holding a club in his right hand and a cup in his left. The base is decorated with acanthus leaves.

(L.F.)

Bibl.: De Caro 1987, p. 88; *Pompei. Abitare* 1996, p. 266, no. 586.

42.-44. Three marble masks

These three masks decorated the nymphaeum of the summer *triclinium* at the House of Neptune and Amphitrite, probably dating back to the Claudian-Neronian period.

42. Marble mask

Inv. no. 78788
Herculaneum, House of Neptune and Amphitrite, *triclinium*.
White marble; l 18; h 26; d 13 cm

43. Marble mask

Inv. no. 78789
Herculaneum, House of Neptune and Amphitrite, *triclinium*.
White marble
l 23; h 33; d 9 cm

44. Marble mask

Inv. no. 78787
Herculaneum, House of Neptune and Anfitrite, *triclinium*.
White marble
l 35; h 32; d. 11 cm

The sculpture is complete except for a chip on the nose and one eyebrow. There is a small hole at the top 1.5 cm in diameter. The recto is roughly carved with a chisel. The eyes are wide open with pupils suggested by holes, and the eyelashes and eyebrows are strongly marked. The forehead is lined and the long curling tresses are held in place by a band round the forehead. Round the tight lips is a moustache and a long curling beard forms thick ringlets with snail motifs at the tips. There is an identical mask of an old man at the *nymphaeum* in the House of the Small Fountain at Pompeii.   (M.P.)

Part of the right ear and the tip of the horns are missing. Multiple traces of red lead paint survive on the beard. The recto is roughly carved with a chisel. This amusing mask represents the god Pan, with animal features including the bearded animal-like head and the goat's horns. Pan is wearing a wreath of leaves and corymbs, he is frowning, his small eyes are holes and his nose is up with wide nostrils. His mouth is a hole, surrounded by a drooping moustache and a long wavy untidy beard. His brow is furrowed and his pupils and nostrils are in the form of holes.

The image of Pan is probably connected to a play about satyrs which was very popular in the Vesuvian area and appears at Herculaneum in the decoration of an elegant marble seat in the *calidarium* in the women's part of the baths at the forum   (M.P.)

The lower part of the nose is missing, which had been added or repaired with a separate piece in antiquity. One curl has a slight chip which has been restored. Traces of red lead paint can be seen on the hair and crown. There are three circular holes below the chin in a triangular formation measuring 1.5 cm in diameter.

This round theatre mask represents the head of a Maenad, with eyes and mouth wide open. The hair is parted down the middle and long curly tresses frame the sides of the face forming three ringlets on either side, made up of four plaited locks of hair. Small spikes of hair at regular intervals form a fringe on the forehead. The eyebrows and eyelashes are strongly marked and the pupils are indicated by round holes. She wears a wreath of flowers intertwined with bands, berries and ivy leaves. (M.P.)

Bibl.: Maiuri 1958, pp. 397 *et seqq.*; Bieber 1961; *Domus Viridaria Horti Picti*, 1992, pp. 119, nos. 36-37; Wallace-Hadrill 1994, pp. 84, 202; Pagano, in *Pitture nella Reggia*, 1999, p. 41, nos. 11-13; Ascione-Pagano 2000, pp. 95 *et seqq.*

45. Oscillum

Inv. no. 76462 (ex 1185)
Herculaneum, House of the Relief
of Telephos.
White marble
Diameter 44 cm; thickness 1 cm
Reconstructed from various fragments.
A few integrations.

Of circular form, it is framed by a
cornice with a double listel and is
sculpted with very light bas-relief only
on the front part. It is decorated with a
figure of a dancing Maenad shown in
profile facing leftwards, the right leg
slightly bent and the left one behind and
balanced on the points of her toes, the
arms stretched out holding the fluttering
hem of her cape, and her head raised
towards the sky turned backwards in a
state of ecstasy. She is balanced on rocks.
She is dressed in a light chiton and a
bodice made of the skin of a panther
that comes over her shoulder and is
wound round her right hip. Her hair,
arranged in long wavy locks, is bound
with a ribbon at the top and is tied back
behind the nape.   (M.P.)

Bibl.: Maiuri, *Ercolano. I nuovi scavi*,
1958, p. 349 *et seqq.*, fig. 278, no. 2;
Domus Viridaria Horti Picti, Naples
1992, p. 118 *et seqq.*, no. 32; Ascione-
Pagano 2000, p. 92, no. 28.

46. Oscillum

Inv. no. 76461 (ex 1184)
Herculaneum, House of the Relief
of Telephos.
White marble
Diameter 45 cm, thickness 1.5 cm
Reconstructed from several fragments.
Many integrations.

102 Of circular form, it is framed by a
cornice with a double listel. It formed a
pair together with the previous one. A
dancing satyr is sculpted on only one
face in extremely light bas-relief; its
profile faces rightwards with curly hair.
The satyr's left arm is held outwards
towards a satyr-like mask balanced on
rocks, while the right arm is held further
back and in its hand a *thyrsus*. The satyr
is naked except for the panther skin
wrapped round the neck which flutters
to the sides.   (M.P.)

Bibl.: Maiuri, *Ercolano. I nuovi scavi*,
1958, p. 349 *et seqq.*, fig. 278, no. 1;
Domus Viridaria Horti Picti, 1992,
p. 119, no. 33; Ascione-Pagano 2000,
p. 92, no. 29.

47a-b. Oscillum

Inv. no. 76458 (ex 1181)
Herculaneum, House of the Relief
of Telephos.
White marble. Traces of a second coat
of paint in blackened red lead
Diameter 29 cm; thickness 3 cm
Slightly fractured on the upper part.

Circular *oscillum*, framed by a flat listel and sculpted in light bas-relief on both faces. On one side of the oscillum is a depiction of Pan with horns and goat's legs, thick unkempt beard and hair, walking to the right in the direction of a lit altar, naked except for the edge of a panther skin that flutters from his left arm. He also holds a covered basket in his left hand, possibly related to the cult of Demeter. His right arm placed further back holds the lower part of a torch, a characteristic element of the cult of the goddess.

The other face is decorated with a young drunken satyr facing towards the right in the direction of a lit altar. He is naked except for the panther skin flowing from his left hip.

The head faces upwards, the hair is thick and curly. In his left hand held out in front of him, he holds a dish with fruit while in his right hand, slightly behind the body and pointing downwards, he holds a torch. (M.P.)

Bibl.: Maiuri, *Ercolano. I nuovi scavi*, 1958, p. 349 *et seq.*, fig. 279; *Domus Viridaria Horti Picti*, 1992, p. 119, no. 34; Ascione-Pagano 2000, pp. 92-93, no. 30a.-b.

48. Bowls containing pigments

Inv. nos. 41505, 41506, 41509, 41633, 41634, 41636, 41639, 41640, 41641, 41650, 48565.

Pompeii, IX 12, 9 (*posticum*).

In a large reception room in a house currently being excavated in Insula 12, Region IX in Pompeii, where the walls were being painted at the time of the eruption in 79 AD, the discovery was made of amphorae full of lime, tools such as compasses in bronze, another tool in bronze to heat the lime and reduce it to very fine powder and a mortar in lava stone with a pestle used to crush the pigments, in addition to numerous small bowls still containing the pigments used by artists for their wall paintings.

In a nearby room other bowls were found, mostly empty, inside a wicker basket which was carried on the back and obviously used to transport the empty bowls back to the workshop, where they would be refilled with pigment.

A total of 57 different sized bowls for pigments were found, of a broadly similar form: a low circular foot and a wide bowl with an inverted, hardly ever everted, rim which made it more functional. However, there were also less common and more distinctive forms. The chemical and mineralogical analysis of the pigments shows the presence in many of the bowls of an organic binding substance, which made the colours suitable for dry fresco work. Some other bowls contained almost pure pigments, without the binder or lime, which suggests the pigments were diluted in pure water for use in wet fresco painting.

Traditionally, seven colours were used: orange, white, blue, yellow, black, red and green. Other shades could be obtained either by using different substances to produce one pigment or by adding another substance to the pigment, for example, dolomite to Egyptian blue to obtain light blue. This

gave the artists a varied palette which could be used to produce many different shades, and would make the colours more or less brilliant as required, using various pigments which provided the same shade but in different tones. For example, for white there was aragonite, cerussite, anular chalk and dolomite; for

yellow there were two different types of yellow ochre; for black there was charcoal; for orange red lead and haematite, obtained by heating yellow ochre; for blue so-called Egyptian blue; for green celadonite, glauconite and malachite; and finally for red crystals of haematite and red ochre.

The bowls shown here have been selected for their shape and the pigments they contain, to give an idea of the vast range which existed.

The pigments are all minerals, except for the black one, which is of vegetable origin, as it is basically carbon. Egyptian blue is not a natural mineral but is produced by synthesis, which made it a very expensive process. (A.V.)

Bibl.: Varone 1995, pp. 124-136; Varone & Bearat 1997, pp. 199-214; Varone, in *Romana Pictura*, 1998, pp. 302-304; Varone, in *Pitture nella Reggia*, 1999, pp. 65 *et sq.*

Organising the exhibition

The exhibition of archeological finds from Pompeii, Herculaneum, Stabiae, Oplontis and Torre del Greco at the Museum of Aberdeen has a dual purpose: to bring together complex cultural and organisational aspects, and to provide a stimulating display and interpretation, with the aim of increasing the cultural awareness of today's visitors and providing a reference point for future visitors.

This is a revised version of the exhibition which took place in 1999 at the Royal Palace of Portici, built in 1738 by Charles of Bourbon, King of Naples following the discovery of Herculaneum in 1710-1711. On display in Aberdeen are artefacts from a wide area around Vesuvius which was affected by the eruption in 79 AD. For most of the visitors on the Grand Tour who came this far south in Italy in the late 18th and early 19th centuries, this was the main attraction of their journey.

This was not only a "Golden Age" of travel chronicles, it was also a romantic landscape, whose attractions (particularly Vesuvius) fired the imagination of artists and resulted in some very imaginative and evocative depictions of "the Mountain".

For these foreigners on the Grand Tour, Italy was a favourite destination for both travelling and painting landscapes, and they marvelled at the recently discovered ancient towns, as a sketch of the Forum of Pompeii by James Giles belonging to the Museum of Aberdeen clearly shows. The sketch owes much to the somewhat exotic themes that Lord Byron celebrates in his fascinating accounts of ancient civilisations, exemplified by the epic poem "Childe Harold's Pilgrimage":

Thy very weeds are beautiful, thy waste
More rich than other climes' fertility.

The theme of the exhibition is to tell a story through symbolic and mythological images and works of the many different manifestations of life and ideas in a particular historical context.

The paintings and sculptures from the Vesuvian towns reveal a continual existential preoccupation with life and death, and with the human and the superhuman: a story which draws on the symbolic and allegorical images from all aspects of everyday life. This is the rationale of the exhibition, which aims to bring out the colour and vitality of the works on display. To achieve this, a new approach to interpretation has been introduced, which includes displays specifically aimed at school parties, both young people and their teachers, so that they can learn more about the works on show, the restoration and conservation methods used and the area where they were created.

The exhibition display consists of three different strands:
– interpretation panels illustrating the chronological development of the styles;
– classification of the works on display according to their provenance;
– techniques of painting, conservation, restoration and documentation with multimedia support to provide more information about the subjects.

Maria Emma Pirozzi, Valerio Papaccio

Glossary

Acroterion	plinth for statues or ornaments placed at ends of pediment, also what stands on them
Aediles	Roman magistrates with policing and surveillance functions
Ambulatio	promenade
Apotheca	store-room
Atrium	open central inner court surrounded by a roof
Cal(i)darium	hot water room in Roman bath
Caupona	tavern
Chiton	long garment in wool worn by ancient Greeks
Chlamys	short light mantle worn by the Greeks and later by the Romans
Compluvium	square opening in the sloping roof of a Roman house
Cryptoporticus	enclosed gallery having walls with openings instead of columns
Cubiculum	a room furnished with a sofa or bed
Cubiculum diurnum	a day room
Ergastula	workhouse
Exedra	semi-circular recess or any apse or niche of a room opening out into a larger room; a parlour or conversation-room
Frigidarium	cold water room in a Roman bath
Gladius	sword
Herm	rectangular pillar terminating in head or bust (after Hermes)
Hortus conclusus	an enclosed garden
Hypocaust(um)	underground chamber or duct of central heating via air flues
Insula	blocks of buildings at Pompeii
Kalathos	Tapering cylindrical head-dress typical of representations of Libyan-Syrian gods in Roman times
Kantharos	Greek drinking cup
Koiné	common language of Greeks from late classical to Byzantine period
Lararium	domestic shrine
Megalografia	a painting with giant figures
Natatio	pool
Negotium	business
Nymphaeum	Roman pleasure house with statues and fountains
Oecus	large reception room
Oikoumene	representation of architecture in painting
Omphalos	circular cavity, usually in stone
Opus incertum	wall covering consisting of small irregular shaped stones
Opus sectile	mosaic made of small regular laminae of marble and stone dovetailing
Opus topiarum	ornamental gardening
Opus vittatum	(or *opera listata*) wall covering consisting of rows of brick alternating with small blocks of tufa stone
Oscillum	a little mask or statue or relief usually hung
Otium	leisure
Ovolo	a wide convex moulding
Palaestra	a school of wrestling
Patera	small flat circular or oval object used for decoration
Pedum	a shepherd's crook
Peristyle	a range of columns surrounding a building or open court
Pinax (pl pinakes)	paintings protected by projecting wooden frames with 4 leaves
Pluteus	parapet
Porticus triplex	a portico with three front columns
Praefurnium	area for heating water in a Roman bath
Rhyton	horn-shaped drinking vessel, often zoomorphic
Suspensurae	small pillars made of bricks or pipes supporting a lower brick floor which heated the baths
Syrinx	pipes of pan
Tablinum	room with one side opening into the *Atrium*
Thyrsus	wand terminating in a pine cone (attribute of Bacchus and satyrs)
Triclinium	Roman dining room
Uraeus	decoration on a Pharaoh's crown in the form of a curved cobra
Viridarium	pleasure garden

Abbreviations

AA	Archäologischer Anzeiger
BdA	Bollettino d'Arte
CrErc	Cronache Ercolanesi. Bollettino del Centro Internazionale per lo studio dei papiri ercolanesi
CrPomp	Cronache Pompeiane
DdA	Dialoghi di Archeologia
EAA	Enciclopedia dell'Arte Antica Classica e Orientale
MededRome	Medelingen van het Nederlandsch historisch Instituut te Rome

NSc	Notizie degli Scavi di Antichità
PBSR	Papers of the British School at Rome
RIASA	Rivista dell'Istituto di Archeologia e Storia dell'Arte
RevArch	Revue Archéologique
RivStPomp	Rivista di Studi Pompeiani
RömMitt	Römische Mitteilungen

Bibliography of the entries

Alessandro Magno. Storia e mito, exhibition catalogue, Rome 1995.

Ascione G.C.-Pagano M., *L'Antiquarium di Ercolano*, Naples 2000.

Barbet A., *La peinture murale romaine*, Paris 1985.

Bastet F.L.-De Vos M., *Proposta per una classificazione del terzo stile pompeiano*, Gravenhage 1979.

Bellezza e lusso. Immagini e documenti dei piaceri della vita, exhibition catalogue, Rome 1992.

Beyen H.G., *Die antike Zentralperspektive*, in "AA", LIV, 1939, pp. 47-72.

Bibier M., *The History of the Greek and Roman Theater*, Princeton 1961.

Blanc N.-Gury F.-Leredde H., *Les images d'Amour: une expérience d'information*, in "RevArch", 2, 1987, pp. 297-334.

Carcopino J., *La vita quotidiana a Roma*, Rome 1987.

De Caro S., *Attività archeologica. Pompei*, in "CrPomp", 5, 1979, p. 178.

De Caro S., *The Sculpture of the Villa of Poppaea at Oplontis: A Preliminary Report*, in *Ancient Roman Villa Gardens*, Dumbarton Oaks 1987, pp. 79-133.

De Caro S., *Villa rustica in località Petraro*, in "RIASA", III, X, 1987, pp. 5-89.

De Vos A. and M., *Die Wanddekorationen der Stabianer Thermen*, in *Die Stabianer Thermen in Pompeij*, Berlin 1979.

De Vos A. and M., *Pompei Ercolano Stabia*, Bari 1982.

Domus Viridaria Horti Picti, exhibition catalogue, Naples 1992.

Elia O., *Pitture di Stabia*, Naples 1957.

Elia O., *Scoperta di dipinti a Stabiae*, in "DdA", 1951, p. 45.

Gallina A., *Le pitture con paesaggi dell'Odissea dall'Esquilino*, in "Studi Miscellanei", 6, 1964.

Helbig W., *Wandgemälde der vom Vesuv verschütteten Städte Campaniens*, Leipzig 1868.

In Stabiano. Cultura e archeologia da Stabiae: la città e il territorio tra l'età arcaica e l'età romana, Castellammare di Stabia 2001.

Italianische Reise. Immagini pompeiane nelle raccolte archeologiche germaniche, exhibition catalogue, Naples 1989.

Jacobelli L., *Le pitture erotiche delle Terme Suburbane di Pompei*, Rome 1995.

Jashemski W.F., *The Gardens of Pompeii, Herculanum and the Villas destroyed by Vesuvius*, I-II, New Rochelle-New York 1993.

Lagi De Caro A., *Alessandro e Rossane come Ares e Afrodite in un dipinto della Casa Regio VI, Insula Occidentalis, n. 42*, in *Studia Pompeiana et Classica in honor of Wilhelmina F. Jashemski*, New Rochelle-New York 1988, I, pp. 75-88.

La Pittura di Pompei, Milan 1991, it. ed. of: Cerulli Irelli M.G.-De Caro S.-Aoyagi M.-Pappalardo V., *Catalogue raisonné of the Pompeian Painting*, I-II, Tokyo 1990.

La Villa San Marco a Stabia, (ed. by Barbet A.-Miniero P.), Naples 1999.

Le Collezioni del Museo Nazionale di Napoli, I.1-I.2, Rome 1989.

Ling R., *Roman Painting*, Cambridge 1991.

Maiuri A., *Pompei. Sculture in bronzo*, in "NSc", 1927, p. 72.

Maiuri A., *Due pannelli vitrei figurati da Pompei*, in "BdA" 4, 46, 1961, p.18 et seqq. Pl. 2.

Maiuri A., *Ercolano. I nuovi scavi*, I, Rome 1958.

Maiuri A., *Una nuova pittura nilotica a Pompei*, in "Atti della Accademia Nazionale dei Lincei. Memorie", series

VIII, Rome 1955, VII, 2, pp. 65-80.

Mielsch H., *Neronische und Flavische Stuckreliefs in den VesuvStaden* in *Neue Forschungen in Pompeii*, Recklinghausen 1975, p. 130.

Miniero P., *Stabiae. Pitture e stucchi delle ville romane*, exhibition catalogue, Naples 1989.

Mols S.T.A.M.-Moormann E., *Ex parvo crevit. Proposta per una lettura iconografica della Tomba di Vestorius Priscus fuori Porta Vesuvio a Pompei*, in "RivStPomp", VI, 1993-1994, pp. 15-52.

Moormann E., *La pittura parietale come fonte di conoscenza per la statuaria antica*, Assen 1988.

Mustilli D., *Botteghe di scultori, marmorarii, bronzieri e caelatores in Pompei*, in *Pompeiana. Raccolta di studi per il secondo centenario degli scavi di Pompei*, Naples 1950, pp. 206-229.

Neapolis. La valorizzazione dei Beni Culturali e Ambientali, I-III, Rome 1994.

Orangerie italiana 1991. The International Fair of Italian Art and Antiques, exhibition catalogue, Bradford-London 1991.

Pagano M., *La villa romana di Contrada Sora a Torre del Greco*, in "CrErc", 21, 1991, pp. 149-186.

Pagano M., *Torre del Greco. Notizie varie*, in "RivStPomp", VI, 1993-94, pp. 35-44.

Pagano M. - Russo F. - Terrasi F. - Tuniz C., *Antropizzazione e attività vulcanica in alcuni siti archeologici di Torre del Greco (NA)*, in *Il sistema uomo-ambiente tra passato e presente*, edited by Albore Livadie C. and Ortolani F., Bari 1998, pp. 221-235.

Paribeni E., *Catalogo delle sculture di Cirene*, Rome 1959.

Peters W.I., *Landscape in Romano-*

110 *Campanian Mural Painting*, Assen 1963.
Pitture e Pavimenti di Pompei, I-III, Rome 1981-1986.
Pittura nella Reggia dalle città sepolte. Affreschi antichi da Pompei, Stabiae, Ercolano, exhibition catalogue, Naples 1999.
Pompéi, exhibition catalogue, Paris 1973.
Pompei, (ed. by F. Zevi), I-II, Naples 1991-1992.
Pompei. Abitare sotto il Vesuvio, exhibition catalogue, Ferrara 1996.
Pompei 1748-1980. I tempi della documentazione, exhibition catalogue, Rome 1981.
Pompeii. Picta fragmenta. Decorazioni parietali dalle città sepolte, exhibition catalogue, Turin 1997.
Pompei. Pitture e mosaici, I-IV, Rome 1990-1994.
Ragghianti C.L., *Pittori di Pompei*, Milan 1963.

Reinach S., *Répertoire des peintures grecques et romaines*, Paris 1992.
Riscoprire Pompei, exhibition catalogue, Rome 1993-1994.
Romana Pictura: la pittura romana dalle origini all'età bizantina, exhibition catalogue, Milan 1998.
Schefold K., *Die Wände Pompejis. Topografisches Verzeichnis der Bildmotive*, Berlin 1957.
Spano G., *La tomba dell'edile C. Vestorio Prisco in Pompei*, in "Atti della Reale Accademia d'Italia. Memorie", serie VII, Rome 1943, III, 6, pp. 237-315.
Spinazzola V., *Pompei alla luce degli Scavi Nuovi di Via dell'Abbondanza (anni 1910-1923)*, Rome 1953.
Terme del Sarno, exhibition catalogue, Rome 1991.
Tran Tam Tinh V., *Essai sur le culte d'Isis à Pompéi*, Paris 1974.
Wallace-Hadrill A., *Houses and Society in Pompeii and Herculaneum*, Princeton 1994.

Varone A., *L'organizzazione del lavoro di una bottega di decoratori: le evidenze dal recente scavo pompeiano lungo via dell'Abbondanza*, in "MededRome", LIV, 1995, pp. 124-136.
Varone A.-Bearat H., *Pittori romani al lavoro. Materiali, strumenti, tecniche: evidenze archeologiche e dati analitici di un recente scavo pompeiano lungo via dell'Abbondanza (Reg. IX, ins. 12)*, in *Roman Wall Painting. Materials, Techniques, Analysis and Conservation (Proceedings of the International Workshop Freiburg 7-9-March 1996)*, Freiburg 1997, pp. 199-214.
Whitehouse H., *In praedis Iuliae Felicis: the Provenance of some fragments of Wall-painting in the Museo Nazionale, Naples*, in "PBSR", XLV, 1977, pp. 52-68.
Zanker P., *Augusto e il potere delle immagini*, Turin 1989.

Printed in May 2001
for Electa Napoli

Photocomposition: Grafica Elettronica, Naples
Printing: SAMA, Quarto (Napoli)
Binding: Legatoria S. Tonti, Mugnano (Napoli)